Math Word Problems

Anita Harnadek

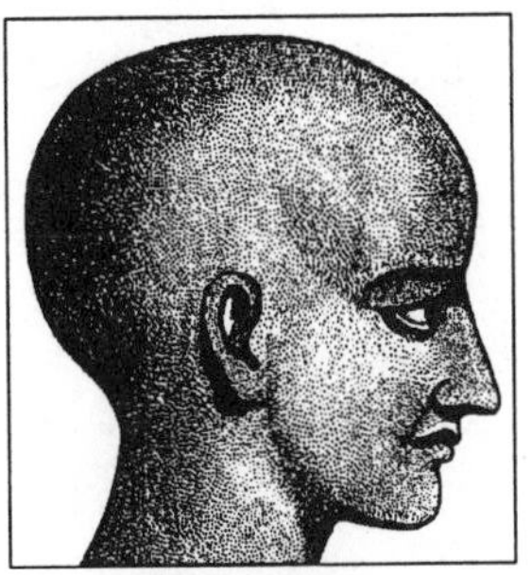

CRITICAL THINKING BOOKS & SOFTWARE

(formerly Midwest Publications)

P.O. Box 448 • Pacific Grove • CA 93950-0448

Phone 800-458-4849 • FAX 408-393-3277

ISBN 0-89455-646-0

Printed in the United States of America

Contents

About This Book

The word problems in a general math textbook are almost always grouped so that the student merely has to use the same operation or solution technique for all problems in a group in order to get the answers. What the student needs, and what this book gives, are problems which are arranged so that they cannot be solved by rote processes, which are arranged so that thought and understanding are required. At the same time, we do not want to give word problems which leave students lost in a confusing maze of words and ideas without any clue of how to take a first step toward solving the problem.

We want students to learn when and how to apply their arithmetic knowledge to solving word problems and later to real-life situations, but once the basic concepts are taught, it can be frustrating to search for word problems that fill these needs. Teachers are always looking for word problems that meet the following criteria:

1. The word problems must be at the arithmetic level of the student.
2. They must be at (or below) the reading level of the student.
3. They must be clearly stated.
4. They should be arithmetically mixed so that the student does not automatically add (or divide in a certain order or subtract or whatever) the numbers given in order to get the answer.
5. They should, at least for the most part, be real-life problems requiring practical applications of arithmetic.

The word problems in this book satisfy the above criteria. Designed to spare the teacher the time and trouble of trying to find or create more word problems, and designed to provide the students with practice using various operations with a particular concept (first six chapters) or with practice using various operations with various concepts (last three chapters), the problems allow you to give your students the kinds of practice problems they need.

All problems are nongraded in content and are written at an elementary reading level, making them suitable for students at any grade level who have been taught the four basic arithmetic operations. In all, there are nine activity chapters:

- Chapter 1: Introductory Word Problems (easy)
- Chapter 2: Whole Numbers (easy to medium)
- Chapter 3: Fractions (easy to somewhat harder)
- Chapter 4: Decimals (easy to harder)
- Chapter 5: Percents 1 (easy to medium)
- Chapter 6: Percents 2 (easy to harder)
- Chapter 7: Mixed Concepts 1 (easy)
- Chapter 8: Mixed Concepts 2 (medium)
- Chapter 9: Mixed Concepts 3 (harder)

These problems allow students to use a variety of arithmetic skills in a variety of contexts to solve problems. The result is that the students really learn when and how to apply their arithmetic knowledge to life situations.

And this is what learning arithmetic is all about, isn't it?

Instructions and Answers

Instructions are provided at the beginning of each chapter. The example problems provided in the instructions can be used as models for solving the problems and to reassure students about what is expected of them in solving the word problems.

Answers for all problems are provided in chapter 10 at the back of the book.

About Chapter 1: Introductory Word Problems

I have found that it can be frustrating to try to teach students to use common sense in solving word problems. You read a problem with the students, and you ask leading questions to try to get them to reason out the answer. Just as you think you're making progress, they ask, "I don't see what all that stuff has to do with it. All I wanna know is, do I add, subtract, multiply, or divide to get the answer?"

It seems the students know they need arithmetic practice and they don't mind that so much, but they can't see why it should be messed up by surrounding it with a lot of words. That is, they seem to think that the purpose of a word problem is to give them more arithmetic practice, rather than to teach them how to apply what they already know.

This first chapter is especially designed for such students, as well as for students who either have not done word problems before or who freeze at the sight of a word problem.

To assist these students, the problems in this chapter all use the same numbers—10 and 40. All answers are $\frac{1}{4}$, $\frac{3}{4}$, 3, 4, 30, 50, or 400. The idea is to make it obvious that the problems are not supposed to provide arithmetic practice, thus allowing students to concentrate on what is being asked and on how to reason out the answers rather than worry about manipulating the numbers afterwards.

The hope is that once the students gain confidence in their abilities to understand, break down, and solve word problems by experiencing success with the problems in this chapter, they can then move without fear to problems which require both reasoning ability and arithmetic ability.

About Chapter 2: Whole Numbers

The problems and answers in chapter 2 are all whole numbers. It will sometimes be necessary for the students to convert dollars to cents in order to do a problem. For example, if a problem requires dividing $5 by 4, then it can be done as a whole number problem by writing $5 as 500¢, resulting in an answer of 125¢. No problem assumes that the students can work with decimals or with fractions.

From my experience teaching remedial arithmetic to high school students, I found that many students did not know things I assumed practically everyone that age knows—common units of measure such as how many seconds are in a minute, how many hours are in a day, how many days are in a week, and how many months are in a year. It is for this reason that problems asking such things are interspersed throughout this chapter. Once the basic question (such as, "How many days are in a week?") has been asked, then a problem a few pages later may assume the student has learned the answer and can use it (as in, "How many days are there in 8 weeks?").

Be careful during the study of problems in this chapter not to ask the students how many weeks are in a month. The common answer, 4, is far enough off from the correct answer, $4\frac{1}{3}$, to make quite a difference in such things as comparing salaries. For example, a salary of $200 a week is a higher salary than a salary of $850 a month, but a person using only 4 weeks in a month would think the $200-a-week salary is considerably lower than the $850-a-month salary.

On the other hand, the common answer of 52 weeks in a year (rather than the correct answer of $52\frac{1}{7}$—or $52\frac{2}{7}$ for leap year) is used here because it is close enough for everyday applications.

Although I realize that most elementary students are now being taught the metric, rather than the English, system of measures,

I feel that public resistance will dictate that the English system still be around for several years. With this in mind, some problems involve inches, feet, miles, quarts, gallons, ounces, and pounds. (Again, many of my remedial arithmetic students did not know how many inches are in a foot, how many ounces are in a pound, etc.) As long as packages and retailers are using such units, the possibilities of getting cheated by not knowing such units are enormous. And, of course, job opportunities are much more limited for people who cannot work with such units.

When you get to problem 62, see if your students can figure out by themselves an easy way to do the problem. A common answer for part *a* will be 3 days, at which time you can point out that if fewer people are working on the job, the job will take more days, not less, to finish. People with some algebra experience may find the problem harder to do than people without such experience. The easy way to do the problem is to multiply 6 carpenters by 9 days and get a starting point of, "It takes a total of 54 carpenter-days to do the job." Now if we have only 2 carpenters working, we divide 54 carpenter-days by 2 carpenters, and we get 27 days to finish the job.

About Chapter 3: Fractions

Some of the exercises are whole number problems with fraction answers, some are fraction problems with whole-number answers, and some are fraction problems with fraction answers. The student is instructed to write as mixed numbers all answers which are improper fractions.

All answers given are exact. If you would rather have your students give approximate answers for some problems, feel free to do so. (For example, it may be less meaningful to a student to know that a jetliner travels at a speed of $651\frac{2}{7}$ kph than to know that it travels at about 651 kph.)

An idea introduced in this chapter is that there are an average of $4\frac{1}{3}$, not 4, weeks in a month. Make sure your students learn and use this information. A salary of $300 a week amounts to $1300, not $1200, a month. Quarterly interest on savings accounts is computed an average of every 13 weeks, not every 12 weeks. There are 52, not 48, weeks in a year.

It disturbs me to hear that some schools are no longer teaching students how to divide by a number containing a fraction, since there are so many problems where such division is needed. (For example, "Porter paid $1.76 for $\frac{2}{3}$ pound of meat. How much a pound was he charged?") To argue that such problems can be done by other methods (and that, therefore, such division is not really needed) seems analogous to arguing that students don't need to know how to multiply, since multiplication can be accomplished by repeated addition. (True, but unnecessarily tedious and time-consuming.) With this in mind, I have ignored the possibility that students may not know how to divide in such cases, and some problems require such division.

About Chapter 4: Decimals

Some problems use whole numbers but have decimal answers; some problems use decimals but have whole-number answers; and sometimes both the problems and the answers are in decimals. The students are told to carry a decimal answer to two places (converting decimals beyond two places into a two-place decimal plus a fraction) unless the answer has only one decimal place. It is assumed that the students know how to work with fractions.

As in Chapter 3, all answers given are exact. Again, if you would rather have your students give approximate answers for some problems, or if you would rather have your students carry the decimal answers to more or fewer places, feel free to do so.

You may wonder why problems were not chosen so that the answers came out "better"—e.g., so that money problems came out with whole cents or speed problems came out with whole mph or kph. The reason they were not so chosen is that everyday life problems come out with "sloppy" answers more often than not, and our teaching the students in school how to cope with such answers will prepare them for the answers they'll get when they start applying what they've learned.

It is important that the students pay attention to what is being asked. Two problems which may seem to have the same answer may have different answers. For example, "Peas sell at 3 cans for $1. (a) You buy 3 cans of them. How much does each can of peas cost you? (b) You buy only one can of them. How much do you pay?" The answer to (a) is $33\frac{1}{3}$¢, and the answer to (b) is 34¢.

As in previous chapters, problems requiring knowledge of everyday units of measure are interspersed throughout other problems.

ABOUT CHAPTER 5: PERCENTS 1

Students who can work with fractions and decimals still have an inordinate amount of trouble with percents. They can answer the questions, "What decimal is $\frac{3}{4}$?" and, "What percent is .75?" and yet not be able to write $\frac{3}{4}$ as a percent. They can know that .2 = 20%. They can work with the problem, "80% of what number is 40?" and can know that 100 – 20 = 80 and yet not have any idea of how to solve the problem, "Jackson paid $40 for a jacket which was on sale for 20% off. What was the regular price of the jacket?" (How many students would solve that problem by taking 20% of $40 = $8, and concluding erroneously that the regular price must be $40 + $8 = $48?!)

The problems in this chapter present many everyday situations. Each situation is approached from more than one viewpoint. For example, if a 20% discount is being offered, one problem states the regular price and asks several questions, while another problem states the discounted price and asks analogous questions. A third problem states both the selling price and the discounted price and asks, among other things, the percent of the discount.

This chapter assumes that the students can work with both fractions and decimals. But since this chapter is meant to be used by students who need a better basic understanding of percents, it avoids, for the most part, fractional percents. It is hoped that the repetitive nature of the problems will help the students learn to work accurately and comfortably with basic percent problems and to have a better understanding of exactly what percents are all about.

Once your students have mastered the problems in this chapter, they should be ready to try the problems in Chapter 6.

ABOUT CHAPTER 6: PERCENTS 2

Although students are instructed to write a non-whole-percent answer as a mixed number rather than as a decimal, the contexts in some problems (such as problems 5 and 16) indicate that decimal percents may be acceptable answers. In such cases, accept either a decimal or a fraction answer. (If you would like your students to write all non-whole-number answers as decimals—e.g., 87.5%, not $87\frac{1}{2}$%—feel free to change the instructions.)

Also, all answers given are exact. If you feel at times that you would rather have your students give approximate answers, there is no reason not to do this.

ABOUT CHAPTERS 7–9: MIXED CONCEPTS 1–3

The problems in Chapter 7: Mixed Concepts 1; Chapter 8: Mixed Concepts 2; and Chapter 9: Mixed Concepts 3 will give the students practice in using not only various operations (addition, subtraction, etc.) but also in using various concepts (whole numbers, fractions, etc.). The problems are mixed so that no one page contains problems which all require the same operation (or series of operations) for solution. One problem might require subtraction of whole numbers, the next require the addition of fractions, the next require computation of a percent, and so on.

Answers given are exact. If you would rather have your students give approximate answers for some problems, there is no reason not to have them do so.

The difficulty level of the problems moves from easy (Chapter 7) through medium (Chapter 8) to harder (Chapter 9). Chapter 7 can be used starting in elementary school. It can also be used with high school remedial arithmetic students. The problems in Chapter 8 require a little more thought and would be appropriate for the average high school student or for gifted junior high and elementary school students. The problems in Chapter 9, too, require only basic arithmetic, but they require more thinking ability than either the Chapter 7 or the Chapter 8 problems and, for the most part, they would be too hard for the elementary school level.

The conditions for the problems in these chapters are the same as the conditions stated for the problems in the other chapters in this series. That is, the problems are meant to be straightforward arithmetic problems with no missing information.

Chapter 1

Introductory Word Problems

INSTRUCTIONS

A. No problem is meant to trick you.

Example

Problem: Darby walked 40 miles at an average rate of 10 miles an hour. How many hours did he walk?

Answer: 4 (Assume the only walking he did was the 40 miles stated in the problem.)

B. No information is missing.

Example

Problem: Ten people ate a total of 40 hamburgers at a party. How many hamburgers did each person eat?

Answer: 4 (It is obvious that we cannot answer the question unless we assume either that the hamburgers were shared equally among the 10 people or that the average number of hamburgers per person is wanted. Since we are told that no information is missing, we assume either or both of these things, and we get an answer of 4.)

C. If the answer is a fraction, write it in reduced form.

Example

Problem: Forty people shared 10 pies. How much did each person get?

Answer: $\frac{1}{4}$ pie (We get an answer of $\frac{10}{40}$ pie, which we reduce to $\frac{1}{4}$ pie.)

1. Garner bought a pair of slacks on sale for $10. The usual price was $40. How much did he save by buying them on sale?

2. Garner bought a pair of slacks on sale for $10 off. He paid $40. What was the usual price of the slacks?

3. Garner bought 10 pairs of slacks at $40 a pair. How much did he spend?

4. Garner bought 10 pairs of slacks on sale for a total of $40. What was the price per pair?

5. Garner bought a pair of slacks on sale for $10. The usual price was $40. How many times greater than the sale price is the amount he saved?

6. Garner paid $10 for one pair of slacks and $40 for another pair. The second pair cost how many times as much as the first pair?

7. At $10 a pair, how many pairs of slacks can Garner get for $40?

8. Carter's old car got 10 miles per gallon of gasoline. His new car gets 40 miles per gallon. How many times greater than the old car's gas mileage is the increase in gas mileage?

9. Carter's old car got 10 miles per gallon of gasoline. His new car's mileage is 40 miles per gallon. How many more miles per gallon does his new car get than his old car got?

10. Carter's car was getting 10 miles per gallon of gasoline. Then he installed a magic gas saver. Now the gas mileage is 40 miles per gallon better. What is the gas mileage now?

11. Carter's old car got 10 miles per gallon of gasoline. His new car gets 40 miles per gallon of gasoline.

a. What fraction of the new car's gas mileage was the old car's gas mileage?

b. How many times better than the old car's gas mileage is the new car's gas mileage?

12. Carter's car gets 40 kilometers per gallon of gasoline. He used 10 gallons of gasoline. How far did he drive?

13. Franklin borrowed $10 from Jeffers. With interest, Franklin had to pay Jeffers a total of $40. How much was the interest?

14. Franklin borrowed $40 from Jeffers. He has paid back $10 so far. How many more $10 payments does he have to make?

15. Franklin made 10 payments of $40 each to Jeffers. How much did Franklin pay Jeffers?

16. Franklin borrowed $10 from Jeffers and $40 from Grayson. How much did Franklin borrow?

17. Franklin borrowed $40 from Jeffers. Then he borrowed $10 from Grayson and paid it to Jeffers. How many more times does he have to borrow $10 from someone in order to pay back Jeffers?

18. Franklin borrowed $40 from Jeffers. He is to pay it back in 10 equal payments. How much is each payment to be?

19. Franklin borrowed $40 from each of 10 different people. How much did he borrow?

20. Franklin borrowed $40 from Jeffers and paid back $10. How much does Franklin still owe Jeffers?

21. Franklin borrowed money from Jeffers. He paid back $40 one time and $10 another time. How much has he repaid so far?

22. Franklin borrowed $40 from Jeffers and the same amount from each of 9 other people. How much did he borrow?

23. Horner spent 10 minutes eating breakfast and 40 minutes eating lunch. How much time did she spend eating breakfast and lunch?

24. Horner spent 10 minutes eating breakfast and 40 minutes eating lunch. How much longer did she spend eating lunch than eating breakfast?

25. For each of the past 10 days, Horner spent 40 minutes eating lunch. How much time did Horner spend eating lunch in the 10 days?

26. A jeweler bought 10 rings. The price was $40 for each ring. How much was spent?

27. A jeweler bought a ring for $10 and sold it for $40. The profit on the ring was how many times as much as the cost of the ring?

28. A jeweler bought a ring for $10 and sold it for $40. How much profit was made?

29. A jeweler paid $40 for one ring and $10 for another. How much was paid for both?

30. A jeweler bought 10 rings for a total of $40. How much was each ring?

31. The Darbys' puppy was 10 inches long when it was eight weeks old. It is 40 inches long now. How much longer is it now than it was at the age of eight weeks?

32. The Darbys measured 40 puppies at 10 inches each. What was the total number of inches measured?

33. The Darbys raise dogs. Their puppies are each 10 inches long. The total lengths of these puppies is 40 inches. How many puppies are there?

34. The Darbys' puppy was 10 inches long when it was eight weeks old. It is 40 inches long now. How many times longer is it now than when it was eight weeks old?

35. When Edwards started as a plumber, her hourly rate was $10. Now it is $40. How many times her old hourly rate is her new hourly rate?

36. Edwards charges $40 for the first hour of work. She charges $10 an hour for any time after the first hour. How much does she charge for the first two hours of work?

37. Edwards raised her hourly rate from $10 to $40. How much higher is her hourly rate now than it was before?

38. Edwards needs $40. She makes $10 an hour. She has worked one hour so far. How much longer does she have to work to make the $40?

39. Last week a restaurant used 10 pounds of coffee. This week the restaurant used 40 pounds of coffee. By how many pounds has the restaurant's use of coffee increased?

40. A restaurant bought 40 cans of coffee at $10 a can. How much did the restaurant pay?

41. A restaurant used 10 pounds of coffee last week and 40 pounds of coffee this week. How much coffee did the restaurant use during these two weeks?

42. A restaurant bought 40 pounds of coffee, 10 pounds at a time. How many times did the restaurant buy coffee?

43. A restaurant uses 40 pounds of coffee a week. The restaurant used 10 pounds of coffee the first day it was open this week. At this rate, how many more days will it be until the usual amount of coffee is used?

44. Last week a restaurant used 10 pounds of coffee to make 40 urns of coffee. On the average, how much coffee was used for each urn of coffee?

45. Giant Store sold 40 ounces of cleaner yesterday. Each can of cleaner weighed 10 ounces. How many cans of cleaner were sold?

AG **46.** Big Store has sold one 10-ounce can of cleaner today. They want to sell a total of 40 ounces of the cleaner. How many more 10-ounce cans of it must they sell?

AG **47.** Big Store sells a 10-ounce can of cleaner for 85¢. Giant Store sells a 40-ounce can of it for the same price. You buy a can of the cleaner from each store. How many ounces of it do you buy?

AG **48.** Big Store sells a 10-ounce can of cleaner for 85¢. Giant Store sells a 40-ounce can of it for the same price. How much more cleaner do you get for 85¢ if you buy it from Giant Store than if you buy it from Big Store?

AG **49.** Big Store sold ten 40-ounce cans of cleaner today. How many ounces of cleaner were sold?

AG **50.** A hand calculator which used to sell for $40 is now being sold for $10. How many more of these hand calculators can you get now for $40 than you used to be able to get?

51. A hand calculator sells for $10. Another one sells for $40. You buy both. How much do they cost?

52. A hand calculator sells for $10. Another one sells for $40. How much more than the first one does the second one cost?

53. A store owner bought 10 hand calculators for a total of $40. How much was each calculator?

54. One hand calculator sells for $10. Another sells for $40. How many times greater than the price of the first one is the difference in price?

55. A dealer bought 40 hand calculators at $10 each. How much did the dealer pay?

56. A hand calculator which used to sell for \$40 is now being sold for \$10. How much less is the price now than it used to be?

57. One hand calculator sells for \$10. Another sells for \$40. How many more of the first kind than the second kind can you get for \$40?

58. A teacher bought 40 pencils 10 different times. How many pencils did he buy?

59. A teacher bought 40 pencils and loaned 10 of them to students. How many did he have left?

60. A teacher bought 40 pencils one time and 10 pencils another time. How many pencils did he buy?

61. A teacher bought 40 pencils, 10 at a time. How many times did he buy pencils?

62. A teacher bought 40 pencils at 10¢ a pencil. How much did he spend?

63. The Harrisons owed $40 on their TV set. Their monthly payments are $10. They have made one payment so far. How many more payments are they to make?

64. The Harrisons paid $40 down on their TV set. They also made one monthly payment of $10. How much have they paid on their TV set so far?

65. The Harrisons still owe $40 on their TV set. They are paying at the rate of $10 a month. How many months do they still have to pay?

66. The Harrisons are supposed to pay $40 a month on their TV set. This month they paid only $10 on it. How much were they short on their payment?

67. The Harrisons bought a used TV set for $40. They paid $10 down and are to make monthly payments of $10 each. How many monthly payments are they to make?

68. The Harrisons owed $40 on their TV set. They paid $10 of it. How much do they still owe?

69. The Harrisons made 10 payments on their TV set. Each payment was $40. How much did they pay so far?

70. Barton made $40 for working two hours. The payroll office took out $10 for various things. How much did Barton get?

71. Barton was supposed to get $40 for working two hours. The payroll office made a mistake and overpaid her by $10. How much did Barton get?

72. Barton makes $10 an hour. She worked 40 hours. How much did she make?

73. Barton made $40 for working ten hours. What was her hourly rate of pay?

74. Barton needed $40. She earned $10 last week. At this rate, how many more weeks will it take her to earn the $40?

75. Barton earned $10 last week and $40 this week. How much did she earn in the two weeks?

76. Amanda and Brian are both in a beginning typing class. Amanda types 10 words a minute. Brian types 40 words a minute. How many times longer does it take Amanda to type something than it takes Brian to type it?

77. Amanda and Brian are both in a beginning typing class. Amanda types 10 words a minute. Brian types 40 words a minute. If they both type for one minute, how many words will they type?

78. Amanda and Brian are both in a beginning typing class. Amanda types 10 words a minute. Brian types 40 words a minute.

a. How many more words a minute does Brian type than Amanda types?

b. How many fewer words a minute does Amanda type than Brian types?

79. There are 40 students in a beginning typing class. Their typing speed is 10 words a minute. If they all type for one minute, how many words will they type?

80. On the way to Big City, Ilson drove at an average rate of 10 mph. On the way back, she drove at an average rate of 40 mph. How much faster was her rate on the way back than on the way going?

81. On the way to Big City, Ilson drove 10 miles. She took the long way coming back and drove 40 miles. How many miles did she drive on the round trip?

82. Ilson rode her bicycle 10 kilometers to Big City on each of 40 days. How many kilometers did she ride?

83. Ilson drove 40 kilometers yesterday and 10 kilometers today. How far did she drive in the two days?

84. Ilson is going on a 40-kilometer drive. She has driven 10 kilometers so far. How many more 10-kilometer legs does she need to drive in order to finish her trip?

85. Ilson drove 40 kilometers to Big City and 10 kilometers to Midville. How many kilometers did she drive?

86. Young bought a pair of shoes for $10. She bought another pair of shoes for $40. How much were the two pairs of shoes?

87. Young bought shoes for $40 at a price of $10 a pair. How many pairs of shoes did she buy?

88. Young owns a shoe store. She bought 40 pairs of shoes at $10 a pair. How much did she pay for these shoes?

89. Young bought a pair of shoes for $10. She started with $40. How many more pairs of the same kind of shoes can she buy?

90. Young thought the price of a new pair of shoes would be $10, but the shoes cost $40. By how much was her estimate off?

91. Young owns a shoe store. She sold 40 pairs of shoes at a profit of $10 a pair. How much profit did she make from these sales?

92. Young sold 10 pairs of shoes for a total profit of $40. What was her profit per pair?

93. Sharon used to be 10 years old. Now she is 40.

a. How much younger did she used to be than she is now?

b. How much older is she now than she used to be?

c. How many years has it been since she was 10 years old?

94. Each of 10 people is 40 years old. What is the sum of their ages?

95. Sharon is now 10 years old. How many more decades does she have to go in order to be 40 years old?

96. Sharon used to be 10 years old. Now she is 40 years old. How many times as old is she now as when she was 10?

97. Forty years ago Sharon was 10 years old. How old is she now?

98. Olsen went on a diet to lose 40 pounds. He has lost 10 pounds so far. What fraction of the 40 pounds has he lost so far?

99. Each person on a diet lost 10 pounds. The total weight lost was 40 pounds. How many people were on the diet?

100. Olsen wanted to lose 40 pounds. He has lost 10 pounds in the first month of the diet. At this rate, how many more months will it take him to lose the desired weight?

101. Olsen went on a diet to lose 40 pounds. He has lost 10 pounds so far. How much does he still have to lose to reach his goal?

102. Ten people went on a diet, each hoping to lose 40 pounds. How much weight do the 10 people hope to lose?

103. Ten people on diets have lost a total of 40 pounds. What is the average weight loss per person?

104. Olsen went on a diet. He lost 40 pounds in the first twelve weeks. He lost 10 pounds in the next six weeks. How much did he lose in the eighteen weeks?

105. You bought one share of stock for $10. You bought another share of stock for $40. How much did you pay for the two shares of stock?

106. You bought some stock for $10 a share. It is now worth $40 a share. How much more is it worth now?

107. You bought 10 shares of stock at $40 a share. How much did you pay?

108. You paid $40 for stock at $10 a share. How many shares did you buy?

109. You had $40. You bought one share of stock for $10. How many more shares of this stock can you buy?

110. You bought 40 shares of stock at $10 a share. How much did you pay?

111. It took you 40 minutes to do the first 20 problems on a test. It took you 10 minutes to do the other problems on the test. How much time did you take to do the test?

112. Yesterday you did 40 problems in 30 minutes. Today you did 10 problems of the same kind in 30 minutes. How many more problems did you do yesterday than today in 30 minutes?

113. You have spent 40 minutes on each of 10 tests in the past two weeks. How much time have you spent on tests in this time?

114. You are doing a 40-problem test. You have finished the first 10 problems in just one minute. At this rate, in how many more minutes will you finish the test?

115. Yesterday you did 40 problems in 30 minutes. Today you did 10 problems in 30 minutes. How many problems did you do in the 60 minutes?

116. You did 40 problems in 10 minutes. How many problems did you do on average in each minute?

117. You got 10 problems wrong on a 40-problem test.

a. What fraction of the problems did you get wrong?

b. What fraction of the problems did you get right?

118. You got 10 problems wrong on a 40-problem test. How many problems did you get right?

119. During the past three weeks, you have done all the problems on 10 tests. There were 40 problems on each test. How many problems did you do?

120. You took 40 minutes to finish a test. You took 10 minutes for each section of the test. How many sections did the test have?

121. You took a 40-problem test. You couldn't do 10 of the problems. How many problems could you do?

122. A two-part test has 40 problems in one section. The other section has 10 problems. How many problems are on the test?

123. Bart was learning to use a meter stick. He measured 10 different things at a total of 40 meters. Each thing measured was the same length. How long was each thing?

124. Bart was learning to use a meter stick. He had something 40 meters long to measure. He measured 10 meters of it and then got tired.

a. What fraction of the job had he done?

b. What fraction of the job did he still have left to do?

c. How many more times does he have to measure 10 meters of the thing in order to finish the job?

125. Bart was learning to use a meter stick. He measured the depth of the yard at 10 meters. The yard was really 40 meters deep. By how much was Bart off?

126. Each of 10 students measured a distance of 40 meters. What was the total distance measured by these students?

127. The telephone company billed 40 customers for $10 each. What was the total billing?

128. Your telephone bill this month was $40. Last month it was $10. How much more was your bill this month than last month?

129. Your telephone bill this month was $40. Last month it was $10. How much was it for the two months?

130. During the last 10 months, you spent $40 making telephone calls. What was the average amount you spent each month for calls?

131. Your telephone bill has been $40 a month for the last 10 months. How much has your total bill been for these months?

132. Your telephone bill last month was $40. You have paid $10 of it. How many more times do you have to pay $10 in order to pay the bill in full?

133. A teacher needed 10 students for one project and 40 students for another project. How many times greater than the number needed for the first project was the difference in the number of students needed for the two projects?

134. A teacher needed 10 students for a project, and 40 students volunteered to help. How many more volunteered than were needed?

135. A teacher needs 40 students for projects, and 10 students are needed for each project. How many projects are there?

136. A teacher needed 10 students for one project and 40 students for another project. How many students were needed for these projects?

137. Forty students volunteered for projects. The teacher used 10 students on each project. Each student was used exactly once. How many projects were there?

138. A teacher needed 40 students for each of 10 projects. How many students were needed?

139. You had $40. You paid $10 for a case of paper. How many more cases of paper can you buy?

140. Paper used to sell for $10 a case. Now it is $40 a case. How much more is it now than it used to be?

141. Paper sells for $10 a case at one place. At another place it sells for $40 a case. If you buy the paper at the first place, how many more cases could you get for $40 than you could get if you buy it at the second place?

142. Paper sells for $10 a case at one place. At another place it sells for $40 a case. You buy a case from each place. How much do you spend?

143. An office bought 10 cases of paper at $40 a case. How much did the office pay?

144. Paper sells for $10 a case. You pay $40 for paper. How many cases of paper do you get?

145. The Everts buy 10 books each time they go to the book store. They always buy 40 books a year. They have been to the book store once this year.

a. How many more books will they buy this year?

b. How many more times will they go to the book store this year?

c. What fraction of this year's book purchases have they already made?

d. What fraction of this year's book purchases do they still have to make?

146. The Everts bought 40 books last year, 10 books for each member of the family. How many people are in the family?

147. The Everts bought 40 books last year. This was 10 more books than they bought the year before. How many books did they buy the year before?

148. The Everts bought 40 books last year. This was 10 fewer than they bought the year before. How many books did they buy the year before?

149. The Everts bought 40 books each year during the last 10 years. How many books did they buy during this time?

150. You buy some wheelbarrows for $10 each. The total is $40. How many wheelbarrows do you buy?

151. You buy a wheelbarrow for $10. You had $40 when you started. How many more wheelbarrows can you buy?

152. You buy a wheelbarrow for $40. You also buy some tools for $10. How much should you give the cashier?

153. You buy a wheelbarrow for $10. You give the cashier a check for $40. How much change do you get?

154. You own a hardware store. You buy 10 wheelbarrows at $40 each. How much do you spend?

155. You buy a wheelbarrow for $10. You had $40 when you started.

a. How much money do you have left?

b. What fraction of the $40 have you spent?

c. What fraction of the $40 do you have left?

156. Farwell paid $10 for a pair of shoes and $40 for a jacket. How much did Farwell spend?

157. Farwell paid $10 for a pair of shoes and $40 for a jacket. How much more than the shoes did the jacket cost?

158. Farwell paid $10 for a pair of shoes and $40 for a jacket. The jacket cost how many times as much as the pair of shoes?

159. The gas tank of your car was empty. It holds 40 liters. You have just added 10 liters to it. How many more times can you add 10 liters to it before it is filled up?

160. The gas tank of your car holds 40 liters. It took 10 liters to fill it up. How much gas was in the tank just before you had it filled?

161. The gas tank of your car is now empty. It holds 40 liters. How many times can you put 10 liters in it before it is filled up?

Chapter 2

Whole Numbers

INSTRUCTIONS

A. No problem is meant to trick you.

Example

Problem: You buy a loaf of bread for 61¢. You give the cashier 75¢. How much change do you get?

Answer: 14¢ (assume the cashier charges you the right amount. Assume you get the right change.)

B. No information is missing.

Example

Problem: You buy a loaf of bread for 61¢ and a package of gum for 20¢. How much do you spend?

Answer: 81¢ (Assume you don't buy anything else. Assume you pay the right amount. Assume there is no sales tax to be added.)

1. Jack bought 2 apples for 15¢ each.
   a. How much did he spend?

   b. He paid for them with two quarters. How much change did he get?

2. Harry gets $5 an hour. How much did he get last week if he worked
   a. 20 hours?

   b. 35 hours?

3. Janet earns $6 an hour. How many hours did she work last week if she earned
   a. $120?

   b. $210?

4. a. How many seconds are in a minute?

   b. How many minutes are in an hour?

   c. How many hours are in a day?

5. The number of days in each month are as follows: January, 31; February, 28; March, 31; April, 30; May, 31; June, 30; July, 31; August, 31; September, 30; October, 31; November, 30; December, 31. How many days does this make in a year?

6. Orange juice sells at 5 cans for 90¢. What is the cost of one can of orange juice?

7. Peter walked 15 blocks to school yesterday. From school, he walked 8 blocks to Nelson's house. From Nelson's house, he walked 10 blocks to the store. From the store, he walked 7 blocks home.
   a. How many blocks did he walk?

   b. There are 20 blocks in a mile. How many miles did he walk?

8. You buy 64¢ worth of things at a store. You give the cashier a dollar bill. How much change should you get?

9. a. How many centimeters are in a meter?

b. How many cents are in a dollar?

c. How many years are in a century?

10. A car went 300 miles in 6 hours. What was its average speed?

11. Pencils sell at 3 for 20¢. What will be the cost of
a. 9 pencils?

b. 21 pencils.

c. 12 pencils?

12. Mr. Gerant bought a pair of slacks on sale.

a–b. The usual price was $22. How much was the sale price if he got

a. $4 off?

b. $10 off?

c–d. The usual price was $18. How much did he get off if he paid

c. $15 for the slacks?

d. $11 for the slacks?

e–f. He paid $15 for the slacks. How much did he get off if the usual price was

e. $20?

f. $29?

g–h. He paid $17 for the slacks. How much was the usual price if he got

g. $10 off?

h. $7 off?

13. A car goes one mile in one minute. How many miles an hour is this?

14. A kicker attempted 43 field goals. She failed to score 19 times. How many times did she succeed?

15. A hand calculator sells for $13. The adaptor for it costs $4 extra. Batteries cost another $1. What is the total needed for all three items?

16. **a.** How many days are in a week?

b. How many weeks are in a year?

c. How many months are in a year?

17. Mary paid 40¢ for a pen. Charles paid 33¢ for the same kind of pen.
   a. How much more did Mary pay for her pen than Charles paid for his?

   b. How much less did Charles pay for his pen than Mary paid for hers?

18. A bus driver collected the same amount from each of 23 passengers. The total was 1035¢. How much did she collect from each passenger?

19. Gasoline costs $2 a gallon. Mr. Brady's car gets 17 miles to a gallon. How far will the car go on $24 of gasoline?

20. A car goes 4 kilometers in 3 minutes. How far will it go in 60 minutes?

21. A hockey goalie made 89 "saves" out of 102 attempts to score against him. How many times did the other team score against him?

22. Viola bought two candy bars for 39¢ each and a package of gum for 20¢.

a. How much altogether did she spend?

b. She gave the cashier a dollar bill. How much change did she get?

23. **a.** Write 3 years as a number of months.

b. Write 60 months as a number of years.

c. Write 4 years 2 months as a number of months.

d. Write 77 months as a number of years and months.

24. What is the area of a rectangular sheet of paper 8 inches wide and 11 inches long?

25. A jetliner went 2,457 kilometers in 3 hours. What was its average speed?

26. Which is the larger salary for a year—$15,000 a year or $1,230 a month?

27. The gas tank of your car holds 21 gallons. How many gallons were in the tank if it took
   a. 14 gallons to fill it up?

   b. 9 gallons to fill it up?

   c. 18 gallons to fill it up?

28. Mr. Owens earned $350 last week. The payroll office withheld $60 for federal income tax, $17 for state income tax, $21 for social security tax, and $10 for union dues. How much did Mr. Owens get?

29. The Simpsons spend an average of $57 a week for food. How much is this a year?

30. Midville High School has 1,265 students. Centerville High School has 897 students. How many more students has Midville High than Centerville High?

31. Mr. Wynn earns 12¢ a minute. How much an hour is this?

32. Jack bought a puzzle for 98¢, a ball for 39¢, a dog collar for 79¢, and a paint brush for 48¢.

a. How much did he spend?

b. He gave the cashier $5. How much change did he get?

33. A catcher got 115 hits out of 500 times at bat. How many times at bat did she fail to get a hit?

34. A bus driver collected 35¢ from each of 19 passengers. How much did he collect?

35. What is the area of a room 12 feet wide and 15 feet long?

36. In hours and minutes, what is the total of
    a. 1 hour 20 minutes and 2 hours 35 minutes?

    b. 2 hours 35 minutes and 1 hour 40 minutes?

    c. 80 minutes and 3 hours 50 minutes?

37. How many seconds are in a day?

38. A surgeon charged $500 for an operation which took 4 hours. How much was this an hour?

39. **a.** Write 3 dollars as a number of cents.

b. Write 500 cents as a number of dollars.

40. **a.** How many inches are in a foot?

b. How many feet are in a yard?

c. How many feet are in a mile?

41. Mrs. Grayton worked 3 hours 20 minutes this morning. She worked 4 hours 40 minutes this afternoon. How long did she work today?

42. Which is the larger salary for a year—$850 a month or $200 a week?

43. The Robinsons make house payments of $350 a month, and $180 of this goes for taxes and insurance. How much is left to count against the interest and the balance due?

44. Marge bought a loaf of bread for 63¢, a dozen lemons at 3 for 31¢, and 5 pounds of apples at 19¢ a pound. She gave the cashier $3. How much change did she get?

45. A car goes one kilometer in one minute. How many kilometers an hour is this?

46. a. Write 5 feet as a number of inches.

b. Write 3 yards as a number of inches.

c. Write 48 inches as a number of feet.

d. Write 24 feet as a number of yards.

47. A concrete pipe has an outside diameter of 16 inches. Its inside diameter is 14 inches. How thick is the pipe?

48. A recipe calls for 1 teaspoonful of vanilla. How much vanilla should be used to make
   a. a double batch of the recipe?

   b. a triple batch of the recipe?

49. How many hours are in a week?

50. a. Find the average of 23 and 35.

   b. Find the average of 15, 7, and 26.

   c. Find the average of 10, 45, 32, 22, and 56.

51. Spinach sells at 2 cans for 55¢. How much will
   a. 4 cans of spinach cost?

   b. 10 cans of spinach cost?

52. Ann counts up her loose change. She has 2 quarters, 4 dimes, 3 nickels, and 7 pennies. How much does her loose change total?

53. The Fabers bought a stereo outfit. The amplifier cost $640. The turntable cost $270. The two speakers cost $610 each. The extra lengths of wire cost $8. What was the total they paid?

54. A jetliner went 1,900 miles in 4 hours. What was its average speed?

55. **a.** How many meters are in a kilometer?

b. How many grams are in a kilogram?

c. How many watts are in a kilowatt?

56. A car's gas mileage is 16 miles per gallon.

a–b. How far will it go on

a. 9 gallons of gas?

b. 20 gallons of gas?

c–d. How many gallons of gas will it use to go

c. 176 miles?

d. 240 miles?

57. The teacher said he would give 10 points extra credit on the next test if Bob did a certain problem correctly. Bob did the problem correctly.

a. Bob's test score without the extra credit was 95. What did the teacher record as Bob's test score?

b. The teacher recorded 95 as Bob's test score. How much was Bob's score without the extra credit?

58. The Millers bought a stove for $420. They paid $100 down. They paid the rest in 8 equal payments. How much was each payment.

59. Opal bought a dog brush for 89¢, 2 balls at 29¢ each, and 3 magazines at 65¢ each.

a. How much did she spend?

b. She gave the cashier $5. How much change did she get?

60. Jill's test scores were 78, 87, 96, and 83.

a. What is the total of these scores?

b. What is the average of these scores?

61. **a.** Write 21 days as a number of weeks.

b. Write 7 weeks as a number of days.

62. Six carpenters can do a job in nine days. Working at the same rate,

a. how many days will it take two carpenters to do the job?

b. how many carpenters will it take to do the job in three days?

63. how many inches are in a mile?

64. **a.** How many ounces are in a pound?

b. How many pints are in a quart?

c. How many quarts are in a gallon?

65. Yeoong-Xin's average score for 5 tests was 89. What was the total score on these tests?

66. Washers sell at 3 dozen for 78¢

a–c. What is the cost of

a. a dozen washers?

b. 6 washers?

c. 960 washers?

d–f. How many washers can be bought for

d. 39¢?

e. 702¢?

f. 65¢?

67. Ms. Baylor made $600 a month for the first 6 months of this year. Then she got a raise of $50 a month. She will not get another raise this year. How much will she make this year?

68. A car goes one mile in two minutes. How many miles an hour is this?

69. Three pounds of hamburger will make 12 hamburgers.

a–c. How many pounds are needed to make

a. 24 hamburgers?

b. 4 hamburgers?

c. 16 hamburgers?

d–f. How many hamburgers can be made from

d. 2 pounds of hamburger?

e. 9 pounds of hamburger?

f. 5 pounds of hamburger?

70. What is the total of

a. 1 foot 8 inches and 3 feet 2 inches?

b. 2 feet 9 inches and 3 feet 7 inches?

c. 79 inches and 2 feet 11 inches (in feet and inches)?

71. A hand calculator is on sale for $6 less than its regular price.

a. The sale price is $11. What is the regular price?

b. The regular price is $15. What is the sale price?

72. How many seconds are in an hour?

73. Ms. Harper bought a power mower on sale.

a–b. The usual price was $113. How much was the sale price if she got

a. $24 off?

b. $38 off?

c–d. The usual price was $145. How much did she get off if she paid

c. $129?

d. $98?

e–f. She paid $99 for the mower. How much did she get off if the usual price was

e. $120?

f. $112?

g–h. She paid $129 for the mower. How much was the usual price if she got

g. $36 off?

h. $72 off?

74. A quarterback attempted 65 passes. Of these, 48 were successful. How many were unsuccessful?

75. Gasoline costs 180¢ a gallon. Ms. Crimm's car gets 16 miles to a gallon. How far will the car go on $36 of gasoline?

76. What is the ratio of

a. 1 pound to 5 ounces?

b. 5 ounces to 1 pound?

c. 36 ounces to 2 pounds?

d. 2 pounds to 36 ounces?

77. Ron's average for 5 tests is 74. What will his average be if he scores 92 on the sixth test?

78. Abby's average for 2 tests is 74. What will her average be if she scores 92 on the third test?

79. a. How many square inches are in a square foot?

b. How many square feet are in a square yard?

c. How many square centimeters are in a square meter?

80. Jefferson strikes out 2 out of every 3 times he bats.

a. He has been at bat 81 times this year. How many times has he struck out?

b. He has struck out 76 times this year. How many times has he been at bat?

81. What's the difference between half a dozen dozen and six dozen dozen?

82. Mr. Jackson is a nurse. He gets $9 an hour on the night shift. He gets $8 an hour on the afternoon shift. He gets $7 an hour on the day shift. How much did he make last week if he worked

a. 40 hours on the day shift?

b. 40 hours on the afternoon shift?

c. 40 hours on the night shift?

d. 16 hours each on the day shift and the afternoon shift and 8 hours on the night shift?

e. 16 hours each on the afternoon shift and the night shift and 8 hours on the day shift?

83. Ms. Anders missed 6 hours of work last week due to being late. She was not allowed to make up the time. There is no overtime pay. If she had worked 36 hours, she would have made $252.

a. What was her hourly rate of pay?

b. How much did she lose by being late to work?

84. A singer is making an average of $1,100 a week this year. At this rate, how many weeks will she have to work this year in order to make at least $28,600?

85. A car went 400 kilometers in 5 hours. What was its average speed?

86. Mrs. Forester makes $8 an hour.

a–b. How much will she make if she works

a. 8 hours?

b. 35 hours?

c–d. How long did she work if she made

c. $120?

d. $312?

87. Mr. Bowdin works in an office. He gets a salary of $360 for a 40-hour week. Yesterday he spent part of his time at work goofing off. He spent 10 minutes on the phone with his wife. He spent 15 minutes on the phone with his son. He spent 20 minutes on the phone trying to find out something about a personal loan. He spent 25 minutes day-dreaming. He spent 20 minutes gossiping with fellow workers. He spent 30 minutes typing a personal letter.

a. How many hours did he goof off?

b. How much is his hourly salary?

c. Not counting the cost of the phone calls, how much money did his goofing off steal from his employer?

d. Suppose there are five other workers in the office and they all goofed off as much as Mr. Bowdin did. How much money did the employer get cheated out of yesterday by his office staff?

88. Pens sell at 3 for 50¢

a–b. How much will

a. 9 pens cost?

b. 21 pens cost?

c–d. How many pens can you buy for

c. $1?

d. $5?

89. A teacher gave a three-problem quiz. The first problem was worth 20 points. The other two were each worth 12 points. How many points was the quiz worth?

90. What was a car's gas mileage (in mpg) if it went

a. 156 miles on 12 gallons of gas?

b. 340 miles on 20 gallons of gas?

91. Two years ago an entertainer worked 30 weeks at an average salary of $900 a week. Last year he worked 22 weeks at an average salary of $1,200 a week.

a. How much did he make two years ago?

b. How much did he make last year?

c. In which year did he make more, and how much more?

92. A car goes 3 miles in 4 minutes. How many miles an hour is this?

93. Eight plumbers can do a job in twelve days. Working at the same rate,

a. how many days will it take four plumbers to do the job?

b. how many days will it take sixteen plumbers to do the job?

c. how many plumbers will it take to do the job in sixteen days?

d. how many plumbers will it take to do the job in thirty-two days?

94. A repair service charges $19 for a house call plus $12 an hour for labor.

a–b. What is the charge for a house call which takes

a. an hour?

b. 3 hours?

c–d. The repair service made a house call. For how many hours was the charge made if the charge was

c. $79?

d. $115?

95. A dozen eggs will make four omelets.

a–c. How many eggs are needed to make

a. 8 omelets?

b. 1 omelet?

c. 9 omelets?

d–f. How many omelets can be made from

d. 2 dozen eggs?

e. 9 eggs?

f. 21 eggs?

96. A concrete pipe has an outside diameter of 20 inches. The pipe is 2 inches thick. What is its inside diameter?

97. **a.** The time is now 9:40. What time will it be 30 minutes from now?

b. The time is now 9:15. What time will it be 55 minutes from now?

c. 25 minutes ago, the time was 1:50. What time is it now?

98. Raoul's average score for 6 tests was 87. The first 5 scores were 70, 100, 100, 98, and 94. What was the score of the sixth test?

99. What is the total of

a. 1 pound 5 ounces and 2 pounds 10 ounces?

b. 2 pounds 11 ounces and 5 pounds 12 ounces?

c. 58 ounces and 3 pounds 7 ounces (in pounds and ounces)?

d. 85 ounces and 70 ounces (in pounds and ounces)?

100. Ms. Tomas drove for 2 hours at an average speed of 60 kph. She drove for another 3 hours at an average speed of 80 kph.

a. How far did she drive?

b. How many hours did she drive?

c. What was her average speed for the whole trip?

101. Ms. Tyler earns $9 an hour. How much a minute is this?

102. A jogger goes a mile in 5 minutes. How many miles an hour is this?

103. The Orlands bought a used car for $3,200. They paid $500 down. The dealer added $900 for interest. The Orlands then paid the balance in 36 equal payments. How much was each payment?

104. A square yard of carpeting sells for $13. You want to carpet a room 13 feet wide by 18 feet long.

a. What is the area of the room in square feet?

b. What is the area of the room in square yards?

c. How much will it cost to carpet the room?

105. At Corbett High School, the ratio of students who take math to those who don't take math is 3 to 1.

a–b. There are 1,230 students at Corbett High who take math.

a. How many Corbett students don't take math?

b. How many students are there at Corbett?

c–d. There are 357 students at Corbett High who don't take math.

c. How many students at Corbett take math?

d. How many students are there at Corbett?

e–f. Corbett High has 1,568 students.

e. How many take math?

f. How many don't take math?

106. The Warners spend $3,380 a year for food. On the average, how much do they spend each week for food?

107. A jogger goes 3 miles in 20 minutes. How many miles an hour is this?

108. **a.** Write 500 centimeters as a number of meters.

b. Write 2 meters as a number of centimeters.

c. Write 4 kilometers as a number of meters.

d. Write 3 kilometers as a number of centimeters.

109. A parking lot charges $3 for the first hour and $1 an hour after that.

a–b. What is the charge for parking there for

a. 2 hours?

b. 5 hours?

c–d. How long was the car charged for if the charge was

c. $6?

d. $11?

110. Mr. Barber made $600 a month for the first 8 months of this year. Then he got a raise of $50 a month. He will not get another raise this year. How much will he make this year?

111. Mr. Hamer drove 120 km from Midville to Centerville. He drove at an average speed of 40 kph. On the way back, he drove at an average speed of 60 kph. What was his average speed for the round trip?

112. You bought 100 shares of stock for $6,000. Two months later the company gave a dividend of one share of stock for every two shares already owned.

a. How much did you pay for each share when you first bought the stock?

b. How many shares did you get as a dividend?

c. How many shares do you own now?

d. What is your average cost per share?

113. On the average, Johnson has made a basket on 4 out of every 5 free throws this year.

a. Johnson has had 100 free throws this year. How many baskets did she make from them?

b. Johnson made 60 baskets from free throws this year. How many free throws has she had?

114. Six electricians can do a job in six days. Working at the same rate,

a. how many days will it take 4 electricians to do the job?

b. how many electricians are needed to do the job in 12 days?

c. how many days will it take 3 electricians to do the job?

115. **a.** Write 2 pounds as a number of ounces.

b. Write 80 ounces as a number of pounds.

116. What is the area of a desktop 3 feet wide and 4 feet long?

117. Maria's class has had 4 tests so far. Maria's average score is 80. What does she need to get on the next test to raise her average to 83?

118. The Palmers bought a piano for $900. They paid $300 down. The interest charge was $72 a year. They paid off the piano in 24 equal monthly payments. How much was each payment?

119. A picture frame is 20 inches long and 14 inches high. The frame is 2 inches wide all the way around. When in the frame, the part of the picture which can show is ______ inches long and _____ inches high.

120. Marge earns $6 an hour. How much a minute is this?

121. What is the total of

a. 1 meter 20 centimeters and 2 meters 70 centimeters?

b. 3 meters 60 centimeters and 4 meters 80 centimeters?

c. 245 centimeters and 2 meters 70 centimeters (in meters and centimeters)?

122. A telephone call between two zones costs 10¢ for the first minute and 8¢ for each minute after that.

a–c. How much does a call between these zones cost if it lasts for

a. one minute?

b. two minutes?

c. eight minutes?

d–f. How long did the call last if the charge for it was

d. 42¢?

e. 82¢?

f. 26¢?

123. Ms. Kramer drove 504 km from Big City to Midville. Her average speed was 72 kph. On the way back, her average speed was 56 kph. What was her average speed for the round trip?

CHAPTER 3

FRACTIONS

INSTRUCTIONS

A. No problem is meant to trick you.

Example

Problem: Washers sell for 20¢ a dozen. How much will you pay for $2\frac{1}{2}$ dozen washers?

Answer: 50¢ (Assume that they cost 20¢ a dozen no matter how many dozen you buy. Assume you pay the right amount.)

B. You are given all the information you need to solve each problem.

Example

Problem: Oranges sell for 90¢ a dozen. You buy 8 oranges. You give the cashier 75¢. How much change do you get?

Answer: 15¢ (Assume you can buy part of a dozen at the price of 90¢ a dozen. Assume you don't buy anything else. Assume the cashier charges you the right amount. Assume the cashier gives you the right amount of change.)

1. Five people shared equally in nine pizzas. How many pizzas did each person get?

2. Nine people shared equally in five pizzas. How many pizzas did each person get?

3. Harry types 85 words a minute. How many words a second is this?

4. a. Write 10 months as a number of years.

   b. Write 35 weeks as a number of years.

   c. Write 5 days as a number of weeks.

5. Ms. Dalton bought a refrigerator for a total of \$400. She paid $\frac{2}{5}$ down.
   a. How much did she pay down?

   b. How much did she still owe?

6. Kevin worked $3\frac{1}{4}$ hours this morning and $2\frac{2}{3}$ hours this afternoon.
   a. How many hours did he work today?

   b. He gets $9 an hour. How much did he get for working today?

7. Mrs. Parker worked $31\frac{1}{2}$ hours two weeks ago. She worked $29\frac{3}{4}$ hours last week. For these two weeks,
   a. what was the total number of hours she worked?

   b. she was paid $8 an hour. What were her earnings?

   c. what was the average weekly number of hours she worked?

   d. how many more hours would she have had to work in order to have worked a total of 80 hours?

8. A salesperson gave away 30 free samples last week. This was $\frac{3}{5}$ of all she started with. How many did she start with?

9. A clerk in a department store gets a salary of $90 a week. She also gets a commission of $\frac{1}{50}$ of her sales. Last week her sales were $7,500. How much did she make last week?

10. A chemist is to mix water and acid in a ratio of 5 to 2.
   a. She wants a total of 14 ml. How much of each should she use?

   b. If she uses 20 ml of acid, how much water should she use?

11. Onions cost 35¢ a pound. Martha bought $5\frac{3}{4}$ pounds of them. How much did they cost?

12. Bob brought $3\frac{1}{3}$ pounds of hamburger for $5. How much was it a pound?

13. Jones bought a case of canned peas for $7. There were 24 cans of peas in the case. What was the average price he paid (in cents) for each can?

14. A recipe for a batch of cookies calls for $1\frac{1}{3}$ cups of flour. Dennis wants to make a double batch. How much flour should he use?

15. Martin worked $3\frac{1}{4}$ hours two days ago. He worked $5\frac{2}{3}$ hours yesterday. He worked $6\frac{1}{2}$ hours today. He got $6 an hour. For these three days,

a. what was the total number of hours he worked?

b. what was the average number of daily hours he worked?

c. how much was he paid?

16. **a.** Write 35 minutes as a number of hours.

b. Write 90 minutes as a number of hours.

c. Write 3 hours 20 minutes as a number of hours.

17. Joe watched an average of $4\frac{1}{5}$ hours of TV every day last week. How many hours of TV did he watch then?

18. Find the cost of a pound of potatoes if $2\frac{1}{4}$ pounds of them cost 72¢

19. A house plan has a scale of $\frac{1}{3}$ inch = 1 foot. What is the house plan size of a room which is 12 feet by $15\frac{1}{2}$ feet?

20. When Derek was 5 years old, he was $1\frac{1}{10}$ meters tall. The next year he grew $\frac{1}{10}$ meter, and the year after that he grew $\frac{1}{20}$ meter. How tall was he when he was 7 years old?

21. Eight people shared equally in $5\frac{1}{2}$ pies. How many pies did each person get?

22. a. Write 17 days as a number of weeks.

b. Write 95 weeks as a number of years.

c. Write 2 years 15 weeks as a number of years.

23. Mrs. Jones wants to use $1\frac{1}{4}$ cans of tomatoes in a meat loaf. She also wants to use $1\frac{1}{5}$ cans of tomatoes for macaroni and cheese.

a. How many cans of tomatoes does she want to use for these two food dishes?

b. She doesn't have any tomatoes now. How many cans of them should she buy in order to have enough for these two food dishes?

24. For problem 23 above, tomatoes cost 40¢ a can.

a. What is the cost of the tomatoes Mrs. Jones wants to use in the two food dishes?

b. What is the cost of the tomatoes Mrs. Jones should buy?

25. Bob bought a record player for $120. He paid $\frac{1}{4}$ down. He paid the rest in 6 equal monthly payments.

a. How much did Bob pay down?

b. How much did he still owe after the down payment?

c. How much was each monthly payment?

26. A car went 330 kilometers in $5\frac{1}{2}$ hours. What was its average speed (in kph)?

27. Jane bought 5 pounds of hamburger; $\frac{3}{10}$ of it fried away as fat and water.
   a. How much hamburger fried away?

   b. How much hamburger was left to eat?

28. Each week Mrs. Barker makes a doll's dress to give away at Christmas. She uses $\frac{1}{5}$ meter of material for each dress. How many meters of material does she use for these dresses in a year?

29. A carpenter was charged for $5\frac{1}{3}$ pounds of nails at 90¢ a pound. He weighed them at home and found he was sold only $4\frac{5}{6}$ pounds of nails.
   a. For how many pounds of nails was he overcharged?

   b. What was the amount of the overcharge?

30. Jake drove 125 kilometers in $2\frac{1}{2}$ hours. What was his average speed?

31. What is the average number of weeks in a month? (Hint: The answer is not 4. How many weeks are in a year? How many months are in a year?)

32. The payroll office says Ms. Eaton worked $29\frac{2}{3}$ hours last week. Ms. Eaton says she worked $31\frac{1}{2}$ hours last week. She gets $9 an hour.

a. How many more hours does Ms. Eaton say she worked than the payroll office says she worked?

b. Suppose the payroll office agrees with Mrs. Eaton. How much more gross pay will she get than if they did not agree with her?

33. Don is giving a party for 20 people. He figures that each person will eat an average of $2\frac{4}{5}$ hamburgers. Based on this,

a. how many hamburgers should he plan to serve?

b. how many pounds of hamburger should he buy if he will make 4 hamburgers from each pound?

34. Cindy worked 3 hours 35 minutes on each of Monday, Tuesday, and Wednesday. She worked 4 hours 10 minutes on Thursday. She worked 5 hours 50 minutes on Friday. She gets $10 an hour. For these five days,

a. how many hours (total) did she work?

b. what was the average number of daily hours she worked?

c. how much was her pay?

d. how much was her average daily pay?

35. A garden hose has an outside diameter of $1\frac{1}{4}$ inches. Its inside diameter is 1 inch. How thick is the hose?

36. A garden hose has an outside diameter of $1\frac{1}{4}$ inches. The hose is $\frac{3}{16}$ inch thick. What is its inside diameter?

37. A garden hose has an inside diameter of $\frac{1}{2}$ inch. The hose is $\frac{3}{16}$ inch thick. What is its outside diameter?

38. Ms. Ordway drove 484 kilometers in $5\frac{1}{2}$ hours. What was her average speed?

39. Bart worked $4\frac{1}{4}$ hours before lunch today. He worked 3 hours 25 minutes after lunch today. How many hours did Bart work today?

40. **a.** Write 7 inches as a number of feet.

b. Write 20 inches as a number of feet.

c. Write $4\frac{1}{3}$ feet as a number of inches.

41. A recipe called for $1\frac{1}{2}$ cups of flour. Hank misread the amount and poured in $1\frac{1}{3}$ cups of flour. To correct his mistake,

a. should he add to or subtract from the amount already poured in?

b. how much flour should he add or subtract?

42. A cook used $2\frac{1}{3}$ cans of tomatoes for chili. She used another $1\frac{3}{4}$ cans of tomatoes for soup. For these two food dishes,

a. how many cans of tomatoes did she use?

b. what was the average number of cans of tomatoes she used?

c. how much did the tomatoes cost if they sell for 36¢ a can?

d. how many cans of tomatoes did she have left if she bought 5 cans of them?

43. Edith is 4 years 10 months older than Frank. Frank is 10 years 3 months younger than Gwen. Is Gwen younger than or older than Edith and by how many years?

44. a. Write 1 month as a number of weeks.

b. Write 3 months as a number of weeks.

c. Write 8 weeks as a number of months.

45. Marty used $1\frac{1}{2}$ feet of wood on one project. He used 10 inches of wood on another project. How many feet of wood did he use on the two projects together?

46. Mark earns $390 a month at his job. On the average, how much is this a week?

47. A jet plane flew 1976 miles in $4\frac{1}{2}$ hours. What was its average speed?

48. A jet plane flew 1976 miles in 4 hours 35 minutes. What was its average speed?

49. On the outside, a wooden crate is 2 feet long, 1 foot high, and $1\frac{1}{2}$ feet deep. The wood is $\frac{1}{4}$ inch thick. What size is the crate on the inside

a. in inches?

b. in feet?

50. Big Company pays a beginning accountant $25,000 a year. This accountant works 2,000 hours for Big Company during this first year. What is this accountant's average hourly salary?

51. Mary bought a 4-pound roast. By weight, $\frac{1}{12}$ of it was bone and another $\frac{3}{20}$ of it cooked away as fat and water.

a. How many pounds did the bone weigh?

b. How many pounds of the roast cooked away as fat and water?

c. How many pounds of meat were left after the roast was cooked?

52. Kelly was $3\frac{1}{2}$ feet tall the year before last. Last year she grew 3 inches. This year she grew 4 inches. How many feet tall is she now?

53. Pam bought a set of tools for a total of $630. She paid $\frac{2}{7}$ down. She paid the balance in 9 equal monthly payments. There was no finance charge.

a. How much did she pay down?

b. How much did she still owe after the down payment?

c. How much was each monthly payment?

d. How much would each monthly payment have been if she had paid $\frac{3}{7}$ down?

54. Betty earns $416 a month at her job. On the average, how much is this a week?

55. On a certain map, two cities which are really 511 kilometers apart are only 14 centimeters apart. What scale is the map using? (Your answer should be, "1 cm = ______ km.")

56. a. Write 58 centimeters as a number of meters.

b. Write $3\frac{1}{4}$ meters as a number of centimeters.

c. Write $3\frac{1}{4}$ meters as a number of kilometers.

57. A car in a traffic jam took $2\frac{1}{2}$ hours to go $1\frac{3}{4}$ miles. What was the car's average speed?

58. A piece of circular tubing has an outside diameter of $13\frac{1}{2}$ centimeters. The tubing material is $\frac{1}{3}$ centimeter thick. What is the inside diameter of the tubing?

59. Joe made \$20 for $4\frac{1}{2}$ hours of work yesterday. He made \$39 for $5\frac{1}{3}$ hours of work today.

a. What was his average hourly earning yesterday?

b. What was his average hourly earning today?

c. What was his average hourly earning for the two days together?

60. Natalie worked 7 hours 25 minutes yesterday. She worked 6 hours 50 minutes today. For these two days,

a. how many hours (total) did she work?

b. what was the average number of hours she worked?

61. Jim worked from 7:25 to 11:45 this morning. He worked from 12:20 to 4:10 this afternoon.

a. How many hours did he work this morning?

b. How many hours did he work this afternoon?

c. How many hours did he work today?

62. When hung, a picture in its frame covers a wall space 18 inches by 24 inches. The frame is $1\frac{1}{2}$ inches wide all the way around. The part of the picture which is showing is _______ inches by _______ inches.

63. A week ago Jonah's teacher assigned homework due next week. Last week Jonah did $\frac{1}{5}$ of the assignment. So far this week Jonah has done another $\frac{1}{3}$ of the assignment. How much does he have left to do?

64. Jefferson makes $240 a week at his job. On the average, how much is this a month?

65. Gasoline sells for 90¢ a half-gallon. How much will $12\frac{7}{10}$ gallons of it cost?

66. The Smiths pay $\frac{1}{4}$ of their total income for housing. They make $30,000 a year. How much do they pay for housing

a. a year?

b. a month, on the average?

c. a week, on the average?

67. On the average, Bonnie spends $4\frac{1}{2}$ hours a week on homework while she is in school. She goes to school 38 weeks a year. How many hours does she spend on homework in a year?

68. A chess board is 15 inches by 15 inches. It is 8 squares wide and 8 squares long (a total of 64 squares). It has a $\frac{1}{4}$-inch border all the way around before the squares start. Then each square is _______ inches by _______ inches.

69. The gas tank of a car holds 18 gallons. The tank is $\frac{1}{3}$ full. How many gallons will it take to fill the tank?

70. Morton averages $780 a month at his job. How much is this a week?

71. Mr. Samuels bought a pair of slacks on sale for $\frac{1}{3}$ off. The regular price was $15. How much was the sale price?

72. Ms. Daniel drove at a steady speed of 80 kph for $4\frac{1}{4}$ hours. How far did she drive in this time?

73. Ms. Todd drove at a steady speed of 80 kph for 3 hours 27 minutes. How far did she drive in this time?

74. Find the average of $\frac{1}{4}$, $\frac{1}{3}$, and $\frac{1}{6}$.

75. Gasoline sells for 90¢ a half-gallon. How many gallons can you get for $12?

76. A wholesaler offers a discount of $\frac{1}{10}$ if you pay cash. Suppose you pay cash. How much will you have to pay for $550 worth of goods?

77. The Wilsons bought a house for $50,000. They paid $\frac{1}{4}$ down.
   a. What fraction of the price did they still owe for the house?

   b. How much money did they still owe for the house?

78. The Barkers spend $\frac{1}{5}$ of their income for food and household supplies. Of this amount, $\frac{3}{4}$ is for food.

a. What fraction of their income is spent for food?

b. What fraction of their income is spent for household supplies?

c. Their income is $20,904 a year. On the average, how much is spent weekly for food? for household supplies?

79. Midville School District bought microcomputers for all of their schools. The total cost was $95,000. The federal government paid for $\frac{9}{10}$ of the total. How much of the total cost, in dollars, was paid by Midville School District?

80. The Watsons spend $\frac{1}{5}$ of their income for food, $\frac{1}{4}$ for housing, $\frac{1}{6}$ for clothing, $\frac{1}{10}$ for medical expenses, and $\frac{1}{5}$ for miscellaneous things. They save the rest. What part of their income do they save?

81. A woman gave $\frac{1}{3}$ of her property to her brother. She then divided $\frac{1}{2}$ of the rest equally among her 4 children.

a. How much of her property did she have left after her gift to her brother?

b. How much of her property did each of her children receive?

c. How much of her property did she have left after her gifts to her children?

82. With tips, Bonnie made $30 from her paper route last week. She spent a total of $6\frac{2}{3}$ hours on her route last week. On the average, how much an hour did she make from it?

83. This year food costs $\frac{1}{8}$ more than it did last year.

a. The Carsons spent $56 a week for food last year. How much would this same food cost them this year?

b. The Darwins are spending $45 a week for food this year. How much would they have spent for this same food last year?

84. A TV set was on sale for $\frac{1}{4}$ off. The usual price was $320. What was the sale price?

85. Noreen's parents agreed to pay $\frac{1}{2}$ of the cost of her new bicycle. Noreen's big sister agreed to pay for $\frac{1}{5}$ of the cost. The bicycle will cost $60. How much money for the bike will Noreen have to find someplace else?

86. Erwin got $\frac{4}{5}$ of the problems right on one test. He got $\frac{7}{12}$ of the problems right on another test. What was the average fraction of problems he got right on these tests?

87. The Jacksons bought a new car for $6,000. They paid $\frac{1}{50}$ of the price as a cash deposit. When their new car was delivered, they traded in their old car, for which they were allowed a credit for $\frac{1}{4}$ of the price of the new car. They also paid (in cash) another $\frac{1}{3}$ of the price of the new car.

a. How much did they pay as a cash deposit?

b. How much money were they allowed for their old car?

c. How much additional cash did they pay when the new car was delivered?

d. How much did they still owe on the new car?

88. Eight plumbers can do a job in twelve days. How many days would it take fifteen plumbers to do the job if they work at the same rate?

89. Joe makes $3 an hour doing odd jobs. How much will he make doing odd jobs if he works

a. $3\frac{1}{2}$ hours?

b. 35 minutes?

c. 7 hours 50 minutes?

90. A car travels 70 kph for 4 hours. It travels 80 kph for another 4 hours. What is its average speed?

91. A car goes 300 km in 4 hours. It goes another 300 km in 5 hours. What is its average speed?

92. A car goes 300 km at an average speed of 70 kph. It goes another 300 km at an average speed of 80 kph. What is its overall average speed?

93. An artist begins a 4-part picture on a clean canvas which is 19 inches wide and 23 inches high. He starts by painting a $1\frac{1}{2}$-inch frame on the canvas. Then he paints a $\frac{3}{4}$-inch line across the middle of the canvas. Then he paints a $\frac{3}{4}$-inch line down the middle of the canvas. There are now 4 sections of the canvas which are unpainted and which are equal in size. Each section is _______ inches wide and _______ inches high.

94. The Altons pay $\frac{1}{3}$ of their income in federal and state taxes. They give another $\frac{1}{10}$ to charities. They put another $\frac{1}{15}$ in a retirement fund. What fraction of their income do they have left for other things?

95. Ramona's brother is $\frac{2}{3}$ as old as she is. She is $\frac{1}{2}$ as old as her father. Her mother is $\frac{5}{6}$ as old as her (Ramona's) father. In ten years, Ramona's father will be 52. How old is

a. Ramona's father?

b. Ramona's mother?

c. Ramona?

d. Ramona's brother?

96. A publisher offers a discount of $\frac{1}{10}$ on all books if you buy 10 copies or more of the same book. Suppose a book's regular price is $9. And suppose you buy 10 copies of it.

a. What is the average price paid for each book?

b. How much did the 10th copy really cost you, and how come?

97. Cheese sells for $1.38 (that's 138¢) a half-pound.

a. How much will $\frac{1}{4}$ pound of this cheese cost?

b. How much will $3\frac{2}{3}$ pounds of this cheese cost?

98. **a.** Write 50 seconds as a number of minutes.

b. Write $\frac{3}{8}$ hour as a number of minutes.

c. Write $\frac{3}{8}$ hour as a number of seconds.

99. You are traveling from Midville to Centerville. It has taken you 2 hours to go $\frac{1}{3}$ of the way. Going at the same rate, how much longer will it take you to get to the $\frac{3}{4}$ point?

100. Joan's class has 15 girls and 12 boys.

a. What fraction of the class is girls?

b. What fraction of the class is boys?

c. In this class, what is the ratio of girls to boys?

d. In this class, what is the ratio of boys to girls?

101. In Jim's class, $\frac{3}{5}$ are boys. There are 12 girls in the class.

a. How many boys and girls are in this class?

b. How many boys are in this class?

102. Put these numbers in order from smallest to largest: $\frac{3}{10}$, $\frac{2}{3}$, $\frac{1}{5}$, $\frac{14}{25}$, $\frac{7}{20}$, $\frac{5}{8}$.

103. An unframed picture is 30 cm wide and 46 cm long. When framed, the part of the picture hidden in the frame is $\frac{2}{3}$ cm wide all the way around. So, the part of the framed picture which is showing is _______ cm wide and _______ cm long.

104. What is the area of a room which is $12\frac{1}{2}$ feet wide and $15\frac{1}{4}$ feet long?

105. What is the volume of a fish tank which is $40\frac{1}{2}$ cm wide, $60\frac{3}{4}$ cm long, and $33\frac{1}{4}$ cm high?

106. A man gave $\frac{1}{2}$ of his property to his oldest son. He then gave $\frac{1}{2}$ of the remainder to his next son. He then gave $\frac{1}{2}$ of what was still left to his third son. The third son gave $\frac{1}{2}$ of what he had received to his own son. How much of the man's property

a. did the second son receive?

b. did the third son receive?

c. did the third son's son receive?

d. did the man have left?

107. A carpenter agrees to build cupboards for $1\frac{1}{2}$ times more than the material costs her. The material costs her $500. For how much did she agree to build them?

108. A cook in a restaurant used $\frac{1}{2}$ pound of coffee to make an urn of coffee. The customers complained that the coffee was too strong. So, the next time the cook used only $\frac{2}{3}$ as much coffee. The customers still complained, so the next time the cook used only $\frac{4}{5}$ as much coffee as he used the second time.

a. How much coffee did the cook use the second time?

b. How much coffee did the cook use the third time?

c. The third time, did the cook use more or less than $\frac{1}{4}$ pound of coffee, and how much more or less?

109. The gas tank of your car holds 21 gallons. You fill it up. You drive 210 miles and fill it up again. This time it takes 14 gallons to fill it. On the average, how many miles did your car go for each gallon of gasoline used?

110. The distance from Midville to Big City is 300 km. You drive there at an average speed of 60 kph. On the return trip, your speed averages 50 kph. What is your average speed for the round trip?

111. You are taking a speed test. You must do 15 problems. On the average, how many seconds are you allowed for each problem if you must be finished in

a. 5 minutes?

b. 3 minutes?

c. $7\frac{3}{4}$ minutes?

112. What is the area (in square feet) of a room which is 15 feet 8 inches wide and 20 feet 7 inches long?

113. A model car is built on a scale of $\frac{1}{4}$ inch = 1 foot. The real car is 17 feet long, 102 inches wide, and 4 feet 10 inches high. How many inches

a. long is the model?

b. wide is the model?

c. high is the model?

114. There are about $2\frac{1}{2}$ centimeters in one inch.

a. About how many centimeters are in $8\frac{1}{3}$ inches?

b. About how many inches are in 67 centimeters?

c. About how many feet are in 90 centimeters?

d. About how many yards are in 750 centimeters?

115. The outside diameter of a washer is $1\frac{1}{8}$ inches. Its inside diameter is $\frac{5}{8}$ inch. How wide is the washer?

116. The outside diameter of a washer is $1\frac{1}{8}$ inches. The washer is $\frac{3}{8}$ inch wide. What is the washer's inside diameter?

117. The inside diameter of a washer is $\frac{1}{2}$ inch. The washer is $\frac{5}{16}$ inch wide. What is the washer's outside diameter?

118. A songwriter agrees to let a recording studio use her song. For this, she is to be paid \$10,000 plus 1¢ for each record made. The recording studio makes $1\frac{1}{2}$ million records of her song.

a. How much is the songwriter to be paid?

b. The songwriter must pay her agent $\frac{1}{10}$ of the amount from question a above. How much does the agent get?

c. How much does the songwriter have left after paying her agent?

119. Norbert is $\frac{1}{3}$ as old as Sharon. Sharon is $\frac{3}{4}$ as old as Tyler. What fraction of Tyler's age is Norbert?

120. On the outside, a cardboard box is 15 inches long, $12\frac{1}{4}$ inches wide, and $9\frac{1}{3}$ inches high. The cardboard is $\frac{3}{8}$ inch thick.

a. What are the measurements of the box on the inside?

b. The box is now full of air. What is the volume of the air in it?

121. **a.** Write 3 quarts as a number of gallons.

b. Write 10 quarts as a number of gallons.

c. Write 15 pints as a number of quarts.

d. Write 18 pints as a number of gallons.

122. There are 231 cubic inches in a gallon.

a. How many cubic inches are in $3\frac{1}{2}$ gallons?

b. How many cubic inches are in a quart?

c. How many cubic inches are in $\frac{2}{3}$ gallon?

123. How many gallons of water are needed to fill

a. a fish tank which is 14 inches wide, 18 inches long, and 12 inches high if the water is to be 2 inches below the top of the tank?

b. a swimming pool which is 60 feet wide, 75 feet long, and 16 feet deep if the water is to be 12 inches from the top of the pool?

124. Carpeting costs $12 a square yard. At this rate,

a. how much does a square foot of carpeting cost?

b. how much will it cost to carpet a room which measures $12\frac{1}{2}$ feet by $16\frac{1}{4}$ feet?

c. how much will it cost to carpet that same room if the carpeting is sold only in full yards? (That is, you can't buy, say, $15\frac{1}{4}$ yards.)

125. On a vacation trip, Nestor drove 485 km the first day, $588\frac{1}{2}$ km the second day, and $600\frac{3}{4}$ km the third day.

a. How many kilometers did he drive (total) these three days?

b. For these three days, what was the average daily number of kilometers he drove?

c–g. There is about $\frac{5}{8}$ mile in one kilometer.

c. About how many miles did he drive the first day?

d. About how many miles did he drive the second day?

e. About how many miles did he drive the third day?

f. About how many miles total did he drive these three days?

g. For these three days, about what was the average daily number of miles he drove?

CHAPTER 4
DECIMALS

INSTRUCTIONS

A. Do not round off any answer unless the problem makes it right to do so.

Example

Problem: Peas sell at 3 cans for $1.01. You buy one can of peas. How much will you be charged?

Answer: $.34 or 34¢ (You can't pay a store a fractional part of one cent.)

B. For part of a dollar, carry the answer to two decimal places. Do not show decimal places for cents.

Example

Problem: You buy 3 cans of peas for $1.01. What is the average price of one of these cans of peas?

Answer: $.33$\frac{2}{3}$ or 33$\frac{2}{3}$¢ (not 33.66$\frac{2}{3}$¢)

C. Suppose an answer is a dollar or more. Then write it as dollars.

Example

Problem: Peas sell at 50¢ a can. How much will 4 cans of peas cost?

Answer: $2 or $2.00 (not 200¢)

D. No problem is meant to trick you.

Example

Problem: You buy meat for $3.87 and give the cashier $5. How much change do you get?

Answer: $1.13 (Assume you pay the full price for the meat. Assume you don't buy anything else. Assume there is no sales tax. Assume you get the correct change.)

E. Assume that a business will round up, not down, when you are to pay. (Note that gas stations are an exception to this rule. The price on the pump is rounded in the usual arithmetic way.)

Example

Problem: Peas sell at 3 cans for $1. You buy one can of peas. How much will you be charged?

Answer: $.34 or 34¢ (not $.33 or 33¢)

F. If an answer is not about money and if the problem does not tell you how many decimal places to use, then carry the division to two decimal places unless you have a zero remainder before then.

Example

Problem: Write $\frac{5}{2}$ as a decimal.

Answer: 2.5 (not 2.50)

Example

Problem: Write $\frac{49}{16}$ as a decimal.

Answer: $3.06\frac{1}{4}$ (not $3\frac{1}{16}$, not $3.0\frac{5}{8}$, not $3.062\frac{1}{2}$, and not 3.0625)

Example

Problem: Compute $\frac{49}{16}$ to three decimal places.

Answer: $3.062\frac{1}{2}$

1. Gasoline sells for 90.6¢ a half-gallon. How much will 6 gallons cost?

2. You buy meat for $5.88 and bread for 65¢. How much do you spend?

3. What is the average of 3, 5, 7, and 8?

4. It takes Bart 1.6 times as long to do a job as it takes you. You can do the job in 35 minutes. How long does it take Bart to do the job?

5. It takes Marty 1.4 times as long to do a job as it takes you. Marty can do the job in 35 minutes. How long does it take you to do the job?

6. Ms. Galloway's gross pay last week was $325.75. The payroll office deducted the following: $19.87 for social security tax, $74.92 for federal income tax, $16.29 for state income tax, $10.50 for union dues, and $11 for miscellaneous. How much will Ms. Galloway's paycheck be?

7. In baseball, a batting average is figured by dividing the number of times at bat into the number of hits. The answer is rounded to three decimal places.
   a. Royer had 3 hits in 10 times at bat. What was his batting average?

   b. Jefferson had 4 hits in 11 times at bat. What was his batting average?

   c. Timons had 6 hits in 19 times at bat. What was his batting average?

8. a. Write 8 ounces as a number of pounds.

   b. Write 17 ounces as a number of pounds.

   c. Write 7.6 pounds as number of ounces.

9. Peaches sell at 5 cans for $1.76. You buy just one can of them. How much are you charged?

10. Mr. Thompson earns $420.21 a week.

a. How much is this a year?

b. How much is this a month?

11. At the end of the semester, Robin owed book fines of $4.35 and lab fees of $2.30. She paid both. She started with $10. How much should she have left?

12. On his fifth birthday, Charles was 1.3 meters tall. The next year he grew 6 centimeters. The following year he grew 8 centimeters. How tall was he on his seventh birthday?

13. Brad counts up his loose change. He has 10 quarters, 4 dimes, 7 nickels, and 14 pennies. What is the total?

14. Paula bought a book for $6.75, paper for $4.78, and pens for $1.76.

a. How much did she spend?

b. She started out with $15.32. How much should she have left?

15. Last year Ms. Trent earned $15,675. This year she will earn $20,250. How many times higher will her income this year be than her income last year?

16. Gasoline sells for 93.7¢ a half-gallon. How much will 14.7 gallons cost?

17. Gasoline sells for 92.4¢ a half-gallon. How many gallons will $4 buy?

18. You buy 8 records for $4.67 each. How much do you spend?

19. Ms. Dawson priced a new car at one dealer at $5,567.29. She priced the same kind of car at another dealer at $5,329.48. Which dealer had the higher price, and how much higher was it?

20. A map uses a scale of 1.5 cm = 10 km. The distance between two cities is really 57 km. How far apart will they be on the map?

21. a. Write 9 inches as a number of feet.

b. Write 8 inches as a number of feet.

c. Write 3.4 feet as a number of inches.

22. Mrs. Unser bought 5 pounds of potatoes at 35¢ a pound. She also bought a dozen oranges at 3 for 28¢.
    a. How much were the potatoes?

    b. How much were the oranges?

    c. How much was the total?

    d. She gave the cashier $10. How much change did she get?

23. What is the average of 2.9, 5.4, and 7.6?

24. Mr. Clark earns $18,750.16 a year. On the average, how much is this a week?

25. Mrs. Clark earns $415.35 a week. How much is this a year?

26. Gasoline sells for 93.7¢ a half-gallon.

a. You buy 7.5 gallons. How much are you charged?

b. You buy 7.6 gallons. How much are you charged?

27. You buy 3 pairs of gloves. The first pair costs $5.87. The second pair costs $9.58. The third pair costs $12.96.

a. How much altogether do you spend?

b. On the average, what is the cost of each pair of gloves you buy?

c. You started out with $30. How much should you have left?

28. You buy 5 records for $5.68 each. You also buy 6 records for $1.39 each. How much do you spend?

29. A fire station sold 38,469 raffle tickets on a new car. The tickets were $1.50 each.
   a. How much did the fire station collect?

   b. They paid $5,800 for the new car they gave away. How much profit did they make?

30. Melissa bought a loaf of bread for 64¢, a dozen eggs for $1.29, and a dozen oranges at 3 for 55¢. She gave the cashier a $10 bill. How much change did she get?

31. Daily News has a circulation of 45,875. Daily Times has a circulation of 58,754. How many times higher is the circulation of Daily Times than that of Daily News?

32. Ms. Norton earns $1,243.71 a month.
   a. How much is this a year?

   b. How much is this a week?

33. **a.** Write 9 months as a number of years.

b. Write 17 months as a number of years.

c. Write 11.7 years as a number of months.

34. Lemons sell at $1.36 a dozen. You buy one lemon. How much are you charged?

35. At the post office, Mark bought different kinds of stamps. He bought thirty-two 15¢ stamps, fourteen 3¢ stamps, and fifty 9¢ stamps. How much did he spend there?

36. Midvale High School has 1.25 times as many students as Corbett High School has.

a. Corbett High School has 1,580 students. How many students does Midvale High School have?

b. Midvale High School has 1,580 students. How many students does Corbett High School have?

37. Larry is 5.75 feet tall. Juanita is 5.5 feet tall. How many inches taller is Larry than Juanita?

38. A water pipe has an outside diameter of 10 cm. The inside diameter is 9 cm. How thick is the pipe?

39. A water pipe has an outside diameter of 12 cm. The pipe is .7 cm thick. What is the pipe's inside diameter?

40. A water pipe has an inside diameter of 11 cm. The pipe is 1.2 cm thick. What is the pipe's outside diameter?

41. The Ralsons made up a budget. They decided to put aside part of each paycheck as follows:

.25 for housing
.2 for food and supplies
.05 for medical expenses
.11 for charities
.17 for clothing
.15 for miscellaneous
.12 for savings

What's wrong with this budget?

42. Garth typed an average of 47.2 words a minute for 11 minutes. How many words did he type in that time?

43. Ms. Bradley earns $7.25 an hour.

a. How much does she earn for working 8 hours?

b–c. She gets time and a half for overtime.

b. How much does she get for 4 hours of overtime?

c. She worked 54 hours one week, of which 14 hours were overtime. How much did she earn that week?

44. Big City's population was 1.8 million more than Midville's. Midville's population was 245,319. What was Big City's population?

45. Mrs. Thomas is 36.75 years old. Mr. Thomas is 34.25 years old. How many months older is Mrs. Thomas than Mr. Thomas?

46. What is the area of a room which is 12.5 feet wide and 14.25 feet long?

47. What is the area of a room which is 11 feet 6 inches wide and 13 feet 3 inches long?

48. Gasoline sells for $1.70 a gallon. How many gallons will $18.75 buy?

49. It took your car 15.8 gallons of gas to go 237 miles. What was the car's average gas mileage (in mpg)?

50. **a.** Write 15 minutes as a number of hours.

b. Write 80 minutes as a number of hours.

c. Write 2.75 hours as a number of minutes.

51. What is the average of 4.65, 3, 8.9, and 5.678?

52. A map uses a scale of 1.5 cm = 10 km. On this map, two cities are 5 cm apart. How many km apart are they really?

53. Roger earns an average of $28.35 a week on his paper route. How much is this a day?

54. Carolyn earns an average of $4.85 a day on her paper route. How much is this a week?

55. Mr. Walters bought 5 pounds of hamburger at $1.48 a pound. But .32 of the total weight cooked away as fat and water.

a. How many pounds of the hamburger cooked away as fat and water?

b. How many pounds of hamburger were left as meat?

c. How much a pound did the meat cost Mr. Walters?

56. A circus sold 5,123 adults' tickets for $3.75 each. It also sold 7,526 children's tickets for $2.25 each. How much did the circus collect from these sales?

57. Light bulbs are on sale at 3 for $1.51. How much will you be charged if you buy just one of them?

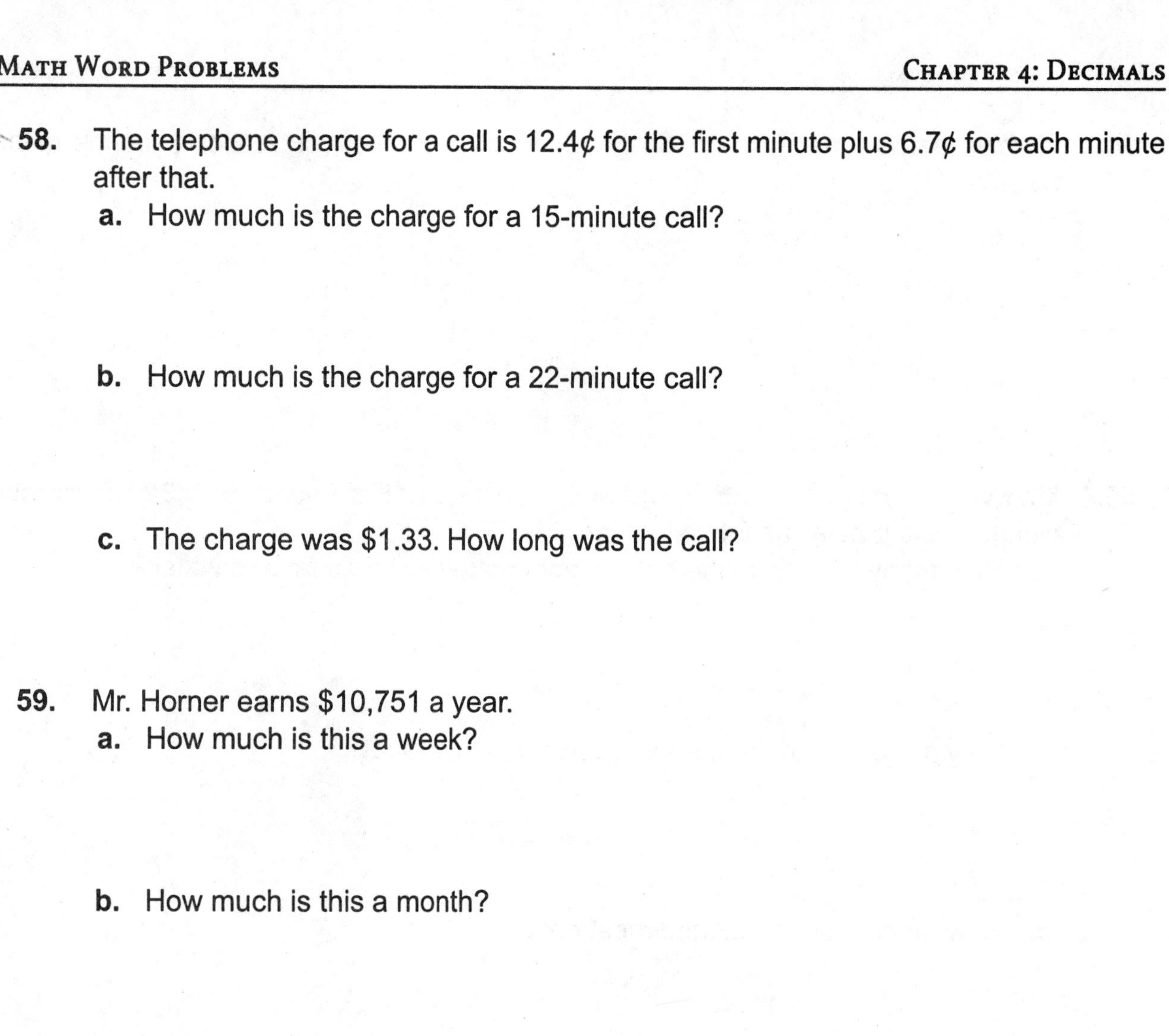

58. The telephone charge for a call is 12.4¢ for the first minute plus 6.7¢ for each minute after that.
   a. How much is the charge for a 15-minute call?

   b. How much is the charge for a 22-minute call?

   c. The charge was $1.33. How long was the call?

59. Mr. Horner earns $10,751 a year.
   a. How much is this a week?

   b. How much is this a month?

60. a. Write 39 weeks as a number of years.

   b. Write 75 weeks as a number of years.

   c. Write 5.2 years as a number of weeks.

61. A car's average gas mileage is 11.8 mpg. At this rate, how far will it go on 17.3 gallons of gas?

62. The label on a can of beans shows the weight to be 484 grams or 1 pound 1 ounce. Based on this, how many grams are in an ounce?

63. Write these numbers in order from smallest to largest: .3, .12, .275, .0678, .2079

64. In baseball, a pitcher's earned run average (ERA) is figured as follows:

- First, multiply 9 by the number of runs scored against him.
- Then divide by the number of innings he pitched.
- The result is rounded to 2 decimal places.

Find Ace's ERA in each of these cases:

a. Ace pitched 4 innings in a game; 3 runs were scored against him.

b. Ace pitched 6 innings in another game; 2 runs were scored against him.

c. Ace pitched 12 innings in another game; 5 runs were scored against him.

d. Ace pitched 2 innings in another game; no runs were scored against him.

65. Figure out Ace's overall ERA for the 4 games in problem 64 above.

66. A school carnival sold 758 tickets for 25¢ each, 2,315 tickets for 10¢ each, and 1,148 tickets for 5¢ each. How much money was collected?

67. What is the average of 5.6, 4.3, and 9.2?

68. A map uses a scale of 1.25 cm = 10 km. Two cities are really 127.8 km apart. How far apart will they be on the map?

69. Last year GIANT SUPERMARKET's sales were 1.7 times as much as the year before.

a. The year before last sales were $4,565,267.50. How much were last year's sales?

b. Last year sales were $5,536,716.57. How much were the sales for the year before last?

70. A store is having a sale. You can get .25 of the regular price off. A dryer usually sells there for $348.80. You buy it while it is on sale.

a. How much discount do you get (in money)?

b. What is the sale price of the dryer?

71. Corbett High School has 1,526 students, of which 1,015 are enrolled in music classes. So the ratio of students enrolled in music classes to those who are not is ________ to 1.

72. A jetliner travels 965 km in 2 hours. What is its average speed?

73. **a.** Write 5 days as a number of weeks.

b. Write 17 days as a number of weeks

c. Write 4.1 weeks as a number of days.

74. Radio station KVT is at 103.5 MHz. Radio station KVW is at 104.2 MHz. How many MHz is station KVT from station KVW?

75. Pat earned $5.80 baby-sitting, $27.40 on her paper route, and $13.85 doing odd jobs. She spent $9.78 on records, $11.65 on jeans, and $11.27 on sweaters.
   a. How much did she earn?

   b. How much did she spend?

   c. How much should she have left?

76. This year Gary will earn 2.5 times as much as he earned two years ago.
   a. Two years ago he earned $4,534.86. How much will he earn this year?

   b. This year he will earn $9,218.50. How much did he earn two years ago?

77. A recipe to serve 4 people calls for 1.5 cups of flour. You decide to use the same recipe to serve a different number of people. How many cups of flour should you use if you make the recipe to serve

a. 10 people?

b. 35 people?

c. 2 people?

d. 3 people?

78. The Gorans bought a refrigerator for $368.75. They paid $110.03 down. They paid the balance in 12 equal monthly payments.

a. How much did they owe after the down payment?

b. How much was each monthly payment?

79. There are 24 cans of beans in a case of beans. The Warners can buy a case of beans for $6.95. If they buy the beans a can at a time, they must pay 31¢ each. How much will they save by buying a case of beans instead of buying them one can at a time?

80. **a.** Write 3 quarts as a number of gallons.

b. Write 17 quarts as a number of gallons.

c. Write 4.5 gallons as a number of quarts.

81. To figure a grade point average in school, we do the following:

- First, we take the final grade from each course taken. We count 4 points for each A, 3 points for each B, 2 points for each C, 1 point for each D, and 0 points for each F.
- Next, we total all the points.
- Finally, we divide this answer by the number of grades. The final answer is rounded to 3 decimal places.

Figure out each student's grade point average.

a. Mary has earned 2 A's, 3 B's, 8 C's, 1 D.

b. John has earned 3 A's, 1 B, 9 C's, 3 D's, and 2 F's.

c. Bonnie has earned 10 A's and 5 B's.

d. Andrew has earned 5 A's and 10 B's.

82. A water pipe has an outside diameter of 10.4 cm. The inside diameter is 7.6 cm. How thick is the pipe?

83. Big City's population is about 9.74 times as much as East City's population.
  a. East City's population is 257,755. About how much is Big City's population?

  b. Big City's population is 1,189.799. About how much is East City's population?

84. Cathy needs another $2,075 to cover her college expenses for the first year. She plans to work during the summer. She has been offered a job paying $4.65 an hour. (Write all answers to the nearest whole number.)
  a. How many hours will she have to work in order to make the money she needs?

  b. Cathy will work 8 hours a day. How many days will she have to work to make the needed money?

  c. Cathy will work 7 hours each day. Each day she works, she will have to pay $1.25 for carfare, $2.25 for lunch, and 75¢ for rental of a uniform. How many days will she have to work to make the money she needs for college?

  d. Cathy will work 8 hours each day. Besides the expenses listed in question c above, the payroll office will withhold $9.67 each day for various taxes. How many days will Cathy have to work to make the money she needs for college?

85. A car travels 3 miles in 30 minutes. What is its average speed (in mph)?

86. A jetliner averaged 327.6 mph for 3 hours and 21 minutes. How far did it go in this time?

87. A map uses a scale of 1.25 cm = 10 km. On this map, two cities are 6.8 cm apart. How many km are they really apart?

88. A large washer has an outside diameter of 11.76 cm. The washer is 1.23 cm wide. What is the washer's inside diameter?

89. The Bartons bought a car for $6,268.35. They traded in their old car for $2,500. They agreed to pay the balance in 36 equal monthly payments. The interest charge for financing the balance was $796.45.

a. What was the balance after the trade-in allowance?

b. What was the balance after the interest charge was added?

c. How much was each monthly payment?

90. In Corbett High School, the ratio of students who take math classes to students who do not take math classes is 1.3 to 1. Corbett High School has 1,472 students.

a. How many do not take math classes?

b. How many take math classes?

91. What is the average of 3.2 and 4.68?

92. **a.** Write 4 hours 25 minutes as a number of hours.

b. Write 39 weeks 6 days as a number of weeks.

c. Write 39 weeks 6 days as a number of years. (Use 365 days in a year.)

93. Nancy had the following test scores: 68, 100, 80, 92, and 91.

a. What was her average score for these tests?

b–c. The teacher rounds the average to the nearest whole number.

b. What average will the teacher show?

c. Suppose the teacher drops the lowest score when computing the average. Now what average will the teacher show?

94. A piece of drawing paper is 46 cm long and 30 cm wide. A border of 2.5 cm must be left all the way around it. The part of the paper which can be used for the drawing is ________cm long and ________cm wide.

95. A jetliner travels 480 km in 36 minutes. What is its average speed (in kph)?

96. Mr. Nestor bought 5.34 pounds of meat at $1.36 a pound. How much was he charged?

97. There are about 28.35 grams in an ounce.

   a. About how many grams are in 5 ounces?

   b. About how many grams are in one pound?

   c. About how many ounces are in 80 grams?

   d. About how many pounds are in 5,286 grams?

98. Ms. Wheeler is a salesperson. She earns a salary of $89.50 a week. She also gets a commission of 4¢ on each dollar she takes in for goods sold. Last week her sales totaled $3,469.25. How much did she earn last week?

99. A parking lot charges $2 for the first half-hour and 75¢ an hour (or part of an hour) after that. Figure out the parking charge for each of the following.

a. Ms. Aston parked her car there $3\frac{1}{2}$ hours.

b. Mr. Uhler parked his car there $2\frac{3}{4}$ hours.

c. Ms. Capra parked her car there $4\frac{2}{3}$ hours.

d. Mr. Farmer parked his car there 45 minutes.

e. Ms. Grebin parked her car there from 8:45 A.M. to 11:25 A.M.

100. In problem 99 above, the charge for Ms. Rogers' car was $7.25. For how long was she charged?

101. The Orlands bought furniture for $1,525.36. They paid $210.15 down. The balance was to be paid in 12 equal monthly payments. The store added a finance charge of $159.83.

a. How much did they owe after the down payment?

b. How much did they owe after the finance charge was added?

c. How much was each monthly payment?

102. **a.** Write 45 centimeters as a number of meters.

b. Write 267 centimeters as a number of meters.

c. Write 1.87 meters as a number of centimeters.

103. It took Mandy 2.3 hours to do a homework assignment. It took her brother 1.7 hours to do the same assignment. How many minutes longer did it take Mandy than it took her brother to do the assignment?

104. The ratio of acid to water in a solution is 3.25 to 1.

a. How much acid should be used to make 17 liters of the solution?

b. The chemist used 5 ml of water for the solution. How much acid should he use?

c. The chemist used 5 ml of acid for the solution. How much water should he use?

105. You buy 24.3 liters of gasoline at 45.5¢ a liter. You also buy 2 liters of oil at 98¢ a liter.

a. What is your total bill?

b. You pay with a $20 bill. How much change do you get?

106. A moving company charges 15¢ a pound plus 50¢ a mile. Their minimum charge is $75. Figure out how much it cost each person to move.

a. Ms. Verind had the company move things weighing 1,500 pounds a distance of 25 miles.

b. Mr. Inness had the company move things weighing 3,523 pounds a distance of 500 miles.

c. Ms. Akers had the company move something weighing 300 pounds a distance of 10 miles.

107. There are 2.54 centimeters in an inch.

a. How many centimeters are in 12 inches?

b. How many centimeters are in a yard?

c. How many inches are in one centimeter?

d. How many inches are in 3 centimeters?

108. Peter bought 3.67 pounds of cheese at $1.38 a pound. How much did he pay for it?

109. Greg's test scores were 89, 70, 80, 100, and 95. The second test counted as double weight. The fourth test counted as triple weight.

a. How many test grades will the teacher count when averaging Greg's test scores?

b. What was Greg's average test score?

c. Suppose the teacher drops the lowest test score. To the nearest whole number, what will Greg's average be?

110. On the inside, a closed box is 15 inches high, 18 inches wide, and 27 inches long.

a. What are its measurements in feet?

b. How many cubic feet of air does it hold?

111. There are about 1.6 km in a mile.

a. About how many km are in 30 miles?

b. About how many km are in 55 miles?

c. A speed of 50 mph is about the same as a speed of ________ kph.

d. About how many miles are there in one km?

e. About how many miles are there in 100 km?

f. A speed of 50 kph is about the same as a speed of ________ mph.

112. What is the exact area of a rectangle 1.3 cm wide and 2.58 cm long?

113. One side of a square measures 1.25 inches. What is the exact area of the square?

114. **a.** Write 75 meters as a number of kilometers.

b. Write 1,776 meters as a number of kilometers.

c. Write 3.25 kilometers as a number of meters.

115. Gasoline sells for 93.8¢ a half-gallon. You buy 7.5 gallons. You give the attendant $20. How much change do you get?

116. A piece of tubing has an inside diameter of 11.37 cm. The tubing is 1.48 cm thick. What is the tubing's outside diameter?

117. The gas tank of your car holds 80 liters. Yesterday it took 57.3 liters to fill the tank. How much was in the tank just before it was filled?

118. A toolmaker measured a part four times. These were the measurements he found: 2.5986 cm, 2.6124 cm, 2.5775 cm, 2.5943 cm. What was the average measurement?

119. A group of eight people bought five pizzas at $4.80 for each pizza. They split the cost equally among themselves. How much did each person pay?

120. A map uses a scale of 1.4 cm = 17 km. On this map, two cities are 11.9 cm apart. How many km are the cities really apart?

121. A map uses a scale of 1.4 cm = 17 km. Two cities are really 123.25 km apart. How far apart are they on the map?

122. A car travels 400 km in 4 hours 39 minutes. What is its average speed (in kph)?

123. A car averaged 45.6 mph for 5 hours 18 minutes. How far did it go in this time?

124. There are about 3.785 liters in a gallon.

a. About how many liters are in 3 gallons?

b. About how many liters are in 4.6 gallons?

c. About how many gallons are in a liter?

d. About how many gallons are in 5 liters?

e. About how many quarts are in a liter?

f. About how many quarts are in 4 liters?

g. Is a liter more than or less than a quart?

125. Harlow ran a mile in 4 minutes. What was his speed in mph?

126. The gas tank of your car holds 21 gallons. You fill it up. You drive 189 miles and fill it up again. This time it takes 15 gallons to fill the tank. What was your car's average gas mileage (in mpg)?

127. To figure out his selling price, a store owner multiplies his cost by 1.25.

a. For how much will he sell something which cost him $97.60?

b. He will sell something for $145.25. How much did it cost him?

Chapter 5
Percents 1

INSTRUCTIONS

A. No information is missing. No problem is meant to trick you.

Example

Problem: Jacobs earned $20,000 last year. This year he got a 20% raise. How much will his income be this year?

Answer: $24,000 (Assume he had no other income. Assume he worked all year both years. Assume he was paid what he earned last year. Assume he will be paid this year's salary this year.)

B. In general, if a percent is not a whole number, write the remainder as a fraction, not as a decimal.

Example

Problem: Rawlins earned $20,000 last year. This year she will earn $24,000. What percent of this year's earnings were last year's earnings?

Answer: $83\frac{1}{3}$ % (not 83.3% or 83.33% or 83.333%, etc.)

1. Dalton is a salesman. He gets a commission of 8% on all the sales he makes. His sales last week were $3,420. How much was his commission?

2. Dalton is a salesman. He gets a commission of 8% on all the sales he makes. His commission last week was $345.20. How much were his sales last week?

3. Dalton is a salesman. He gets a commission on all the sales he makes. His sales last week were $4,400. His commission on these sales was $308. What percent of the sales was his commission?

4. Daniels paid 20% down on a $6,000 car. How much did he pay down?

5. Daniels paid $6,000 as a 20 % down payment on a boat. How much was the boat?

6. Daniels paid $6,000 down on a $40,000 house. What percent of the price of the house was the down payment?

7. North is a saleswoman. She gets a weekly salary of $100. She also gets a commission on 6% on all the sales she makes. Her sales last week were $3,420. How much did she earn last week?

8. North is a saleswoman. She gets a weekly salary of $100. She also gets a commission of 6% on all the sales she makes. She earned $347.20 last week. How much were her sales last week?

9. North is a saleswoman. She gets a weekly salary of $100. She also gets a commission on all the sales she makes. She earned $323.20 last week. Her sales last week were $5,580. What percent of the sales was her commission?

10. A bank pays 8% annual interest on a savings certificate.
 a. What monthly rate of interest does it pay?

 b. What quarterly rate of interest does it pay?

11. A bank pays 7% annual interest on a savings certificate. Smith buys a $4,000 certificate. How much interest does he get on this each year?

12. Smith invested $5,000 in a savings certificate. He gets $450 a year in interest on the certificate. What yearly interest rate does the certificate pay?

13. Smith put some money in a savings certificate which earns 8% a year. The yearly interest is $600. How much did Smith invest?

14. Marge's score on a test was 85%. She had 34 problems right.
   a. How many problems were on the test?

   b. What percent of the problems on the test did Marge get wrong?

   c. How many problems did Marge get wrong?

15. Marge took a test with 40 problems on it. She got 36 right.
   a. What was Marge's score on the test?

   b. What percent of the number of problems on the test did Marge get right?

   c. How many problems did Marge get wrong?

   d. What percent of the number of problems on the test did Marge get wrong?

16. Marge's score on a test was 84%. The test had 25 problems on it.

a. What percent of the problems did Marge get wrong?

b. How many problems did Marge get right?

c. How many problems did Marge get wrong?

d. What percent of the number of problems wrong was the number of problems on the test?

e. What percent of the number of problems wrong was the number of problems right?

f. What percent of the number of problems on the test was the number of problems Marge got wrong?

17. A dealer offers to sell you a car listed at $7,000 for $6,860.

a. How much discount is the dealer offering?

b. What percent discount is the dealer offering?

c. What percent of the list price is the price the dealer quotes you?

18. A dealer offers to sell you a car at 3% off the list price. He quotes you a price of $6,596.

a. The price quoted you is what percent of the list price?

b. How much is the list price?

c. The list price is what percent of the price quoted you?

d. How much money is the discount offered you?

19. At two different dealers, you price a new car which has a list price of $7,500. One dealer offers you a 3% discount. The other offers you a 2% discount.

a. How much money is the first dealer's offered discount?

b. How much money is the second dealer's offered discount?

c. How much money would you save by buying the car at the first dealer's place?

d. What is the percent difference in discounts offered? Take this percent of the list price. Is the answer the same as your "c" answer?

e. If you buy from the first dealer, what percent of the list price do you pay?

f. How much do you pay if you buy the car from the first dealer?

g. If you buy from the second dealer, what percent of the list price do you pay?

h. How much do you pay if you buy the car from the second dealer?

i. Subtract your "f" answer from your "h" answer. Is the result the same as your "c" answer?

20. **a.** What percent is $\frac{3}{4}$?

b. What percent is $\frac{1}{4}$?

21. **a.** Write 20% as a fraction.

b. Write 80% as a fraction.

22. Bradley's car was getting 20 mpg. She had it tuned up. Now it gets 25 mph.

a. What percent of the new gas mileage was the old gas mileage?

b. What percent of the old gas mileage is the new gas mileage?

c. What percent of the new gas mileage is the improvement in gas mileage?

d. What percent of the old gas mileage is the improvement in gas mileage?

23. Bradley's car was getting poor mileage. She had it tuned up. Now it gets 20 mpg. This is a 25% improvement over the old gas mileage.

a. What percent of the old gas mileage is the new gas mileage?

b. What was the old gas mileage?

c. What percent of the new gas mileage was the old gas mileage?

d. What percent of the new gas mileage is the improvement in the gas mileage?

24. **a.** Write $\frac{1}{10}$ as a percent.

b. Write $\frac{2}{10}$ as a percent.

c. Write $\frac{3}{10}$ as a percent.

d. Write $\frac{4}{10}$ as a percent.

e. Write $\frac{5}{10}$ as a percent.

f. Write $\frac{9}{10}$ as a percent.

25. Bradley's car was getting 20 mpg. She had it tuned up. Now the gas mileage is 20% better than it was before.

a. What percent of the old gas mileage is the new gas mileage?

b. What is the new gas mileage?

c. What percent of the new gas mileage was the old gas mileage?

d. What percent of the old gas mileage was the improvement in gas mileage?

26. You buy a new car. The unpaid balance is $4,000. You arrange to finance the car for two years. The finance charge is figured on the unpaid balance. The charge is $720.

a. What is the finance charge for one year?

b. What percent of the unpaid balance is the yearly finance charge?

c. What percent of the unpaid balance is the total finance charge?

27. **a.** Write $\frac{1}{1}$ as a percent.

b. Write $\frac{2}{2}$ as a percent.

c. Write $\frac{3}{3}$ as a percent.

d. Write $\frac{4}{4}$ as a percent.

e. Write $\frac{10}{10}$ as a percent.

f. Write $\frac{389}{389} \times \frac{247}{247}$ as a percent.

28. You buy a new car. The unpaid balance is $5,000. You arrange to finance the car for two years. The finance charge is figured on the unpaid balance. The charge is $1,100.

a. What percent of the unpaid balance is the finance charge?

b. What percent of the unpaid balance is the yearly finance charge?

29. The yearly finance charge on a new car is 8% of the original unpaid balance. You buy a new car. After the down payment, you still owe $5,000. How much is the finance charge for

a. one year?

b. two years?

c. three years?

d. four years?

e. six months?

f. eighteen months?

g. thirty months?

h. forty-two months?

30. The yearly finance charge on a new car is 8% of the original unpaid balance. You buy a new car. The finance charge for three years is $1,560.

a. What is the finance charge for one year?

b. What was the original unpaid balance on the car?

31. You buy a used car. The unpaid balance is $2,000. You arrange to finance the car for three years. The finance charge is figured on the unpaid balance. The charge is $720. What percent of the unpaid balance is the yearly finance charge?

32. Midstate levies a sales tax on all retail sales. Big Store's retail sales, including the tax, were $2,201.80. The retail sales, not including the tax, were $2,137.67.

a. How much tax was collected?

b. What percent of the sales, not including the tax, were the sales including the tax?

c. What percent is the Midstate sales tax on retail sales?

33. Midstate levies a 4% sales tax on all retail sales. Big Store's retail sales, including the tax, were $4,616.04.

a. How much were Big Store's retail sales, not including the tax?

b. How much tax does Big Store owe Midstate?

34. Midstate levies a 4% sales tax on all retail sales. Big Store's retail sales, not including the tax, were $4,616.04. How much sales tax does Big Store owe Midstate?

35. Crawford made $10,000 last year. She will make $15,000 this year.

a. What percent of this year's earnings were last year's earnings?

b. What percent of last year's earnings are this year's earnings?

c. By what percent did last year's earnings increase?

36. Crawford made $10,000 last year. She got a 25% raise this year.

a. What percent of last year's earnings are this year's earnings?

b. How much is she making this year?

c. What percent of this year's earnings are last year's earnings?

37. Crawford is making $21,000 this year. This is a 12% improvement over her salary last year.

a. What percent of last year's salary is this year's salary?

b. How much did Crawford make last year?

c. What percent of this year's salary was last year's salary?

38. Garner is a machinist. She used to make 50 parts an hour. Now, she makes 112% as many parts per hour as she used to make. How many parts per hour does she make?

39. Garner is a machinist. She used to make 50 parts an hour. Now, she makes 112% more parts per hour than she used to make. How many parts per hour does she make?

40. Garner is a machinist. She used to make 50 parts an hour. Now, she has improved this production by 10%.

a. What percent of the old hourly number of parts is the new hourly number of parts?

b. How many parts does she now make each hour?

41. Garner is a machinist. She makes 66 parts an hour. This is a 10% improvement over the number of parts per hour she used to make.

a. What percent of the old hourly number of parts is the new hourly number of parts?

b. How many parts did she used to make each hour?

c. What percent of the new hourly number of parts was the old hourly number of parts?

42. Garner is a machinist. She used to make 40 parts an hour. Now, she makes 50 parts an hour.

a. What percent of the old hourly number of parts is the new hourly number of parts?

b. What percent of the old hourly number of parts is the improvement in production?

c. What percent of the new hourly number of parts is the old hourly number of parts?

43. A publisher sells books to dealers for 25% less than the list price. The price of a book sold to a dealer is $15.

a. What percent of the list price is the price to the dealer?

b. How much is the list price of the book?

c. What percent of the $15 price does the dealer pay?

d. What percent of the $15 price is the list price?

e. What percent of the price charged the dealer is the list price?

f. What percent of the list price does the dealer pay?

44. **a.** Write 150% as a fraction.

b. Write 50% as a fraction.

45. A publisher sells books to dealers for 25% less than the list price. The list price of a book is $15.

a. How much discount on this book would a dealer get?

b. What price would a dealer pay?

c. What percent of the list price would a dealer pay?

d. What percent of the price charged the dealer is the list price?

46. A publisher charges a dealer $6.60 for a book which has a list price of $11.

a. What percent of the list price is the price charged the dealer?

b. What percent of the list price is the dealer's discount?

c. What percent of the list price is $4.40?

d. What percent of the price charged the dealer is the list price?

47. a. Write $\frac{3}{4}$ as a percent.

b. Write $\frac{6}{8}$ as a percent.

c. Write $\frac{9}{12}$ as a percent.

d. Write $\frac{12}{16}$ as a percent.

e. Write $\frac{30}{40}$ as a percent.

f. Write $\frac{75}{100}$ as a percent.

48. A piece of metal is .2 cm thick. Jason measured it as .17 cm.

a. What percent of the real thickness was the measured thickness?

b. What percent of the measured thickness is the real thickness?

c. What percent of the real thickness was the amount of error in the measured thickness?

49. Jason measured the thickness of a piece of metal as .02 cm. The metal was really .2 cm thick.

 a. What percent of the measured thickness was the real thickness?

 b. What percent of the real thickness was the measured thickness?

 c. By what percent of the real thickness was the measured thickness in error?

50. A piece of metal is .2 cm thick. Jason measured it as 10% thinner than it was. What was Jason's measurement of the metal?

51. A piece of metal is .2 cm thick. Jason measured it as 10% thicker than it was. What was Jason's measurement of the metal?

52. Edwards bought a TV set on sale for $300. Its usual price was $375.

 a. What percent of the usual price was the sale price?

 b. What percent of the usual price did Edwards save by buying the TV set on sale?

53. Edwards bought a $500 TV set on sale at a 15% discount.

a. How much was the discount?

b. How much did she pay for the TV set?

c. What percent of the usual price was the sale price?

d. How much did Edwards save by buying the TV set while it was on sale?

54. Edwards paid $387 for a TV set which was on sale at a 14% discount.

a. What per cent of the usual price was the sale price?

b. What was the usual price of the TV set?

c. What percent of the sale price was the usual price?

55. You clip a coupon from the newspaper which gives you 25¢ off the regular price of a package of dog food. The dog food usually costs 75¢. What percent of the regular price do you save by using the coupon?

56. You clip a coupon from the newspaper which offers you a $1 refund from the manufacturer if you mail it to them with a label from their product. You buy the product for $3.23 plus 4% sales tax. You mail the coupon and label to the manufacturer at a cost of 15¢ for the stamp and 1¢ for the envelope. The manufacturer sends you a check for $1.

a. How much did it cost you to send the coupon to the manufacturer?

b. How much profit did you make from sending the coupon to the manufacturer?

c. How much sales tax did you pay on the product?

d. How much (total) did you pay for the product at the store?

e. What percent of the total you paid was your profit?

f. How much did the product end up costing you?

g. What percent of the original sale price (including tax) was your actual cost of the product?

57. **a.** Write 95% as a fraction.

b. Write 5% as a fraction.

58. Woods gets a hit 25% of the times she bats. She has 38 hits.

a. How many times has she batted?

b. How many times at bat has she failed to get a hit?

59. Three out of every four times at bat, Woods fails to get a hit.

a. What percent of her times at bat does Woods not get a hit?

b. What percent of her times at bat does Woods get a hit?

60. Woods got 57 hits out of 190 times at bat.

a. What percent of the times at bat did Woods get a hit?

b. What percent of the times at bat did Woods not get a hit?

61. Woods gets a hit 32% of the times she bats. She has batted 150 times.
    a. How many hits did she get?

    b. How many times at bat did she not get a hit?

62. Borton sued Jones. Borton's attorney charged 30% of the amount the court made Jones pay Borton. The court made Jones pay Borton $50,000.
    a. How much did the attorney get?

    b. How much did Borton have left?

    c. What percent of the awarded amount did Borton have left?

    d. What percent of the awarded amount did the attorney get?

    e. The amount of money Borton paid the attorney was what percent of the amount Borton got to keep?

63. Borton sued Jones. Borton's attorney charged 30% of the amount the court made Jones pay Borton. After Borton paid the attorney, Borton had $42,000 left.

a. What percent of the awarded amount did Borton have left?

b. What was the awarded amount?

c. What percent of the amount Borton had left was the awarded amount?

d. How much did the attorney get?

64. a. Write $\frac{1}{5}$ as a percent.

b. Write $\frac{2}{5}$ as a percent.

c. Write $\frac{3}{5}$ as a percent.

d. Write $\frac{4}{5}$ as a percent.

65. A TV station charges 50% more for running an ad during prime time than for running the same ad in the afternoon. An ad costs $3,375 during prime time.

a. What percent of the charges for an afternoon ad is the charge for a prime time ad?

b. How much does the $3,375 prime time ad cost as an afternoon ad?

66. A TV station charges 50% more for running an ad during prime time than for running the same ad in the afternoon. An ad costs $2,700 in the afternoon. What is the cost of running the same ad during prime time?

67. At a certain TV station, an ad which costs $1,900 in the afternoon costs $2,660 during prime time.

a. What percent of the afternoon cost is the prime time cost?

b. What is the difference (in money) between the two costs?

c. What percent of the afternoon cost is the difference in costs?

d. What percent of the prime time cost is the afternoon cost?

68. a. Write 225% as a fraction.

b. Write 125% as a fraction.

c. Write 25% as a fraction.

69. Andrews bought a ring for $10 off the usual $40 price.

a. What percent discount did she get?

b. What percent of the usual price did she pay?

c. How much was the discount (in money)?

d. How much did she pay (in money)?

70. Andrews bought a ring for $10 off the usual price. She paid $30 for it.

a. What was the usual price of the ring?

b. What percent off the regular price did Andrews get?

c. What percent of the usual price did Andrews pay?

d. What percent of the regular price was the discounted price?

e. What percent of the discounted price was the regular price?

71. Andrews bought a $40 ring at a 30% discount.

a. How much was the discount?

b. How much did Andrews pay for the ring?

c. What percent of the regular price did Andrews pay?

d. What percent of the price Andrews paid was the regular price?

72. Al takes $40% longer to do a job than you take. The job takes you 20 minutes.

a. How long does the job take Al?

b. What percent of the time the job takes you to do does the job take Al to do?

c. What percent of the time the job takes Al to do does the job take you to do?

73. Al takes 63 minutes to do a job which takes you only 45 minutes.

a. What percent of the time the job takes you to do does the job take Al to do?

b. How much longer (in minutes) does the job take Al than it takes you?

c. As a percent, how much longer does the job take Al than it takes you?

74. Al takes 40% longer to do a job than you take. Al takes 49 minutes to do the job.

a. What percent of the time you take for the job does Al take?

b. How much time do you take for the job?

c. How many minutes longer than you take does Al take for the job?

d. What percent of the time the job takes you is the extra time the job takes Al?

75. For Werner's car, the air pressure in the tires is supposed to be 24 psi. The air pressure is really 30 psi.

a. What percent of the ideal air pressure is the real air pressure?

b. By what percent are the tires overinflated?

c. What percent of the real air pressure is the ideal air pressure?

76. For Werner's car, the air pressure in the tires is supposed to be 25 psi. The tires are underinflated by 20%

a. What percent of the ideal air pressure is the real air pressure?

b. What is the air pressure in the tires?

77. On Werner's car, the air pressure in the tires is 26 psi. This is 4% higher than the ideal air pressure.

a. What percent of the ideal air pressure is the real air pressure?

b. What is the ideal air pressure?

78. **a.** Write 1800% as a fraction.

b. Write 180% as a fraction.

c. Write 18% as a fraction.

d. Write 1.8% as a fraction.

79. This year a house is worth $50,000. Last year it was worth $40,000.

a. What percent of last year's value is this year's value of the house?

b. In money, what is the difference in the two values of the house?

c. What percent of last year's value is the difference in the two values?

d. What percent of this year's value is last year's value of the house?

80. This year a house is worth 10% more than it was worth last year. Last year the house was worth $44,000.

a. In money, how much more is the house worth this year?

b. How much is the house worth this year?

c. What percent of last year's value is this year's value of the house?

d. What percent of this year's value was last year's value of the house?

81. **a.** Write 7000% as a fraction.

b. Write 700% as a fraction.

c. Write 70% as a fraction.

d. Write 7% as a fraction.

e. Write .7% as a fraction.

82. This year a house is worth 10% more than it was worth last year. This year the house is worth $44,000.
   a. What percent of last year's value is this year's value of the house?

   b. How much was the house worth last year?

   c. What is the difference between this year's value and last year's value of the house?

   d. What percent of last year's value is the difference in values?

83. Loring's dental insurance pays 60% of the cost of dentures. Loring had dental plates made which cost a total of $950.
   a. How much of the cost did the insurance company pay?

   b. What percent of the cost did Loring pay?

   c. How much did Loring pay?

84. Loring's dental insurance pays 60% of the cost of dentures. Loring paid $344 for dentures.

a. What percent of the total cost did Loring pay?

b. What was the total cost of the dentures?

c. How much of the cost did the insurance company pay?

85. Big Store offers a 20% discount on all purchases after the first $20 total. At Big Store, you buy goods totaling $30 (before the discount).

a. On how much of the total do you get a discount?

b. How much is the discount?

c. How much do you pay?

86. Big Store offers a 20% discount on all purchases after the first $20 total. You buy goods there and pay them $60.

a. How much of the amount you paid was for goods bought at the regular price?

b. How much of the amount you paid was for goods bought at the discounted price?

c. On goods you bought at a discounted price, what percent of the regular price did you pay?

d. What was the regular price of the goods you bought at a discount?

e. What was the regular price of all the goods you bought?

87. **a.** Write $\frac{2}{1}$ as a percent.

b. Write $\frac{3}{1}$ as a percent.

c. Write $\frac{4}{1}$ as a percent.

d. Write 5 as a percent.

e. Write 11 as a percent.

f. Write 251 as percent.

g. Write 3897 as a percent.

88. A thrift shop sells clothes for 75% less than the usual price. Ms. Harper bought a dress there for $6.

a. What percent of the usual price did Ms. Harper pay?

b. What was the usual price of the dress?

c. How much did Ms. Harper save?

89. A thrift shop sells clothes for 75% less than the usual price. At the thrift shop, Ms. Harper bought a dress whose usual price was $20.

a. How much did she pay for the dress?

b. How much did she save by buying the dress at the thrift shop?

c. What percent of the usual price did she save by buying the dress at the thrift shop?

90. Ms. Harper bought a dress at a thrift shop for $5. The usual price of the dress was $12.50.

a. What percent of the usual price did Ms. Harper pay?

b. What percent of the usual price was the discount Ms. Harper got from the thrift shop?

c. How much did Ms. Harper save by buying the dress at the thrift shop?

91. The local drug store offers a 50% discount on medicines sold to senior citizens. Mr. Gorman, a senior citizen, bought medicine for $2.50 there.

a. What percent of the usual price did Mr. Gorman pay?

b. What is the usual price of the medicine he bought?

c. What percent of the price paid by Mr. Gorman is the usual price of the medicine?

92. The local drug store offers a 50% discount on medicines sold to senior citizens. Mr. Gorman, a senior citizen, bought medicine there which had a regular price of $8.60. How much did Mr. Gorman pay for the medicine?

93. The local drug store offers a discount on medicines sold to senior citizens. Mr. Gorman, a senior citizen, bought medicine there for $5.40. The usual price of the medicine was $9.

a. How much less than the usual price did Mr. Gorman pay?

b. What percent of the usual price did Mr. Gorman pay?

c. What percent of the usual price was the discount given Mr. Gorman?

CHAPTER 6

PERCENTS 2

INSTRUCTIONS

A. No problem is meant to trick you.

Example

Problem: A store advertises a 20% discount on all books. The regular price of one book is \$5. What is the sale price?

Answer: \$4 (Assume the book is in the store mentioned. Assume the advertising was truthful. Assume the store did not normally give a 20% discount on books.)

B. No information is missing.

Example

Problem: A jacket usually sells for \$40. You buy it at 15% off. How much do you spend?

Answer: \$34 (Assume you don't buy anything else. Assume you pay the right amount. Assume there is no sales tax.)

C. If a percent answer does not come out to a whole number, write it as a mixed number, not as a decimal.

Example

Problem: What percent of 80 is 70?

Answer: $87\frac{1}{2}$ % (not 87.5%)

1. Angel's age is 75% of Heather's age. Heather is 8 years old. How old is Angel?

2. What percent of one minute is
   a. 30 seconds?

   b. 45 seconds?

   c. 50 seconds?

3. Of the field goals attempted, the Rams have succeeded 13 times. They have been unsuccessful 7 times. What percent of the time have they been
   a. successful?

   b. unsuccessful?

4. A newspaper interviewed 780 people last week. Of these people, 95% knew that George Washington was the first president of the United States.
   a. How many people knew who the first president of the United States was?

   b. How many people did not know who the first president of the United States was?

5. A left fielder has made errors 5.1% of the time. What percent of the time has she not made errors?

6. A car manufacturer says it will increase the prices of its new cars by 4%. One of its cars now sells for $6,240. What will the price be when the increase takes effect?

7. A loan shark makes loans at an interest rate of 10% a week. The interest is on any amount you owe him, including interest. You borrow $100 from him. How much do you owe him at the end of
   a. one week?

   b. two weeks if you don't pay anything before that?

   c. three weeks if you don't pay anything before that?

   d. four weeks if you don't pay anything before that?

   e. two weeks if you paid $30 at the end of the first week?

   f. three weeks if you paid $40 at the end of the first week and $50 at the end of the second week?

8. Mr. Ingle earned $370 last week. Of this, 6.14% was withheld for social security tax. How much was withheld for this tax?

9. A pound is what percent of

a. 8 ounces?

b. 24 ounces?

c. 32 ounces?

10. Last year Mr. James made $14,850.

a. This year he got a 12% raise. How much is he making this year?

b. This year he got a raise and is making $16,038. What percent was his raise?

11. You bought some stock a year ago for $1,200. How much is it worth now if its value

a. has increased 10%?

b. has decreased 10%?

c. has increased 5%?

d. has increased $\frac{1}{2}$%?

e. has decreased .3%?

f. has increased 50%?

12. The Lions have made field goals 60% of the times they attempted them. They have attempted 15 field goals. How many times have their attempts been unsuccessful?

13. Ms. Fraser's salary is $450 a week. A percent of the $450 is withheld for income tax. How much is withheld if the payroll office withholds

a. 14%?

b. 19%?

c. 22.2%?

14. You bought a new car a year ago for $6,340. It is worth 23% less now.

a. How much has it decreased in value?

b. How much is it still worth?

15. A store advertises, "$\frac{1}{3}$ off the regular price for everything inside!"

a. What percent discount are they offering?

b. What percent of the regular price is the sale price?

16. An ice hockey goalie has a "saves" record of 71.2%. What percent of the time did his opponents succeed when they tried to score against him?

17. A salesperson works on a commission basis. She gets 3% of all the sales she makes. How much did she make last week if her sales were

a. \$100?

b. \$10,000?

c. \$85,250?

18. Last week the salesperson from problem 17 above made \$438.72. How much were her sales?

19. The Comptons were injured in an accident which was not their fault. An attorney said her charge for taking the case to court would be 30% of whatever the Comptons were awarded.

a. Suppose the Comptons were awarded \$40,000. How much did the attorney get?

b. Suppose the Comptons lost the case and were not awarded anything. How much did the attorney get?

20. The Tigers won 20 games, tied 2 games, and lost 18 games. What percent of the games did they

a. win?

b. tie?

c. lose?

21. You bought some stock a year ago for $2,500. By what percent has the value increased if the stock is now worth

a. $3,000?

b. $2,600?

c. $2,550?

d. $5,000?

22. What percent of a foot is

a. 1 inch?

b. 3 inches?

c. 8 inches?

23. Handy Suppliers offers a 3% discount if the customer pays within 10 days. You bought supplies totaling $548.30 from them. How much will you save if you pay them within 10 days?

24. Groceries now cost 12% more than they did last year.

a. Last year food cost the Athertons $45 a week. How much does that same kind of food cost this year?

b. This year the Bortons are spending $77 a week for food. How much did the same kind of food cost last year?

25. Martin earns $12,000 a year; Nelson earns $15,000 a year.

a. By what percent are Nelson's earnings more than Martin's?

b. By what percent are Martin's earnings less than Nelson's?

26. You have a new job. At the end of each of the first three years, you will get a 10% raise. You will not get other raises in this time. Your starting salary is $12,000 a year.

a–c. How much is your yearly raise at the end of

a. the first year?

b. the second year?

c. the third year?

d. How much is your yearly salary at the start of the fourth year?

27. You buy a new car for $5,700. You pay $2,200 down. You finance the rest for 3 years. The yearly interest is 8% of the original unpaid balance.

a. How much is the interest charge for a year?

b. How much is the interest charge you must pay?

28. Two years ago typing paper sold for $6 a ream. Now it is $10.50 a ream. By what percent did the price increase?

29. Of the students in the Corbett School District, 40% ride the bus to school.
 a. The district has 6,150 students. How many ride the bus to school?

 b. How many students does the district have if 3,296 students ride the bus to school?

 c. If 5,115 students do not ride the bus to school, how many students does the district have?

30. Shoes are on sale at 25% off. How much does a pair of shoes
 a. sell for now if the regular price is $12.60?

 b. usually sell for if the sale price is $12.60?

31. A dryer costs 11% more this year than last year.
 a. Last year the dryer cost $220. How much is it this year?

 b. This year the dryer costs $349.65. How much was it last year?

32. It is customary to leave a 15% tip for good service in a restaurant. What is the usual tip for good service if the bill totals
   a. $8?

   b. $9.60?

   c. $25?

33. Large candy bars are on sale at $33\frac{1}{3}$ % off. How much does a candy bar
   a. cost on sale if its regular price is $1.50?

   b. usually cost if its sale price is 90¢

34. Of the students in the vocal music class, 70% took the class last year, too.
   a. The class had 80 students. How many did not take the class last year?

   b. There are 33 students who did not take the class last year. How many are in the class?

35. What percent of one gallon is

a. 1 quart?

b. 4 quarts?

c. 10 quarts?

36. Last week a container of milk sold for 65¢. Now it is 70¢.

a. What percent of last week's price is this week's price?

b. By what percent did the price increase?

c. What percent of this week's price was last week's price?

d. By what percent was last week's price lower?

37. Mr. Garner's weekly salary is $400. A percent of the $400 is withheld for income tax. What percent was withheld if the amount withheld was

a. $50?

b. $72?

c. $90.40?

38. Ms. Harrison's weekly salary is $375. The payroll office withholds 17% for income tax. At the end of the year, Ms. Harrison's income tax return shows a total of $3,846 tax which should have been paid. Does Ms. Harrison owe more income tax, or does she have a refund coming, and how much?

39. Paper prices are now 1.5 times what they were three years ago. What percent increase is this?

40. A first baseman has made successful plays 85.8% of the time this season.
a. What percent of the time has he made errors?

b–c. He has made 168 plays so far this season.
b. How many have been successful?

c. How many errors has he made?

41. Last year Ms. Howard made $15,000. This year she will make $18,000.
a. What percent of last year's salary is this year's salary?

b. By what percent did her salary increase?

c. What percent of this year's salary was last year's salary?

d. By what percent was last year's salary less?

42. An artist sold 20% of the pictures he painted.
a. He painted 50 pictures. How many did he sell?

b. He sold 18 pictures. How many did he paint?

43. Corbett High School's new stadium seats 3,000 people. The old stadium seated only 1,800 people. By what percent has the seating capacity increased?

44. Of 50 attempted passes by a quarterback, 30 have been completed and 5 have been intercepted by the other team. What percent of the total number of attempted passes

a. have been completed?

b. have been intercepted?

c. have not been completed?

d. have been successful?

e. have been unsuccessful?

45. A foot is what percent of

a. 1 inch?

b. 8 inches?

c. 24 inches?

46. Big Corporation has a suggestion box for its employees to use. The employee gets a bonus of 4% of whatever the company saves during the first year the suggestion is used. How much bonus does an employee get if his or her suggestion saves __________ during the first year it is used?

a. $100,000

b. $235,000

47. How much is 20% of $\frac{3}{5}$ of 600?

48. A store advertises 20% off everything inside. You go inside and buy

a. a dryer. The regular price is $250. How much is the sale price?

b. a refrigerator. The sale price is $360. What is the regular price?

c. a TV set with a regular price of $425 and a microwave oven with a regular price of $305. How much do you pay (total)?

d. a stereo set on sale for $240 and a kitchen range on sale for $450. What is the combined regular price of these two items?

49. The Carlins bought a set of storm windows for their house. They paid $100 down. They paid the balance in 12 equal payments of $78.40 each. The windows would have been a total of $940 if they had paid cash. What annual rate of interest was charged on the original unpaid balance?

50. What percent of one meter is

a. 1 centimeter?

b. 13 centimeters?

c. 84 centimeters?

51. A basketball player made field goals 65% of the times she tried them.

a. She tried to make a field goal 140 times. How many did she make?

b. She made 104 field goals. How many times did she try?

52. A TV station received 5,000 letters about a program it showed: 65% of the writers said they liked the program; 30% said they didn't like it; 5% didn't say whether or not they liked it but complained about the commercials shown.
   a. How many said they liked the program?

   b. How many said they didn't like the program?

   c. How many complained about the commercials?

53. It was a week before the deadline for getting new license plates. On her way home from work, Ms. Elton counted 365 cars with new plates and 190 cars with old plates. To the nearest whole number, what percent of the cars she counted
   a. showed new license plates?

   b. still showed old license plates?

54. A grocer sells goods for 25% more than they cost her.
   a. What is her selling price of goods which cost her $12.60?

   b. What was her cost of goods she sold for $75?

55. What is the monthly rate of interest if the yearly rate is

a. 12%?

b. 18%?

c. 10%?

56. What percent of one hour is

a. 20 minutes?

b. 30 minutes?

c. 40 minutes?

57. Darwin takes 20% longer to do a job than you take.

a. The job takes you 15 minutes. How long does it take Darwin?

b. The job takes Darwin 45 minutes. How long does it take you?

58. Big Supermarket said its sales increased 30% during last month's advertising campaign.
  a. The sales averaged $131,287.50 before the campaign. How much did they average during the campaign?

  b. The sales averaged $146,381.82 during the campaign. How much did they average before the campaign?

59. Loretta needs to get a score of at least 70% on the next test.
  a. The test will have 20 problems. How many must she get right?

  b. She must get at least 21 problems right. How many problems will the test have?

  c. She can get no more than 12 problems wrong. How many problems will the test have?

60. The national unemployment rate is 5.4%. The "work force" is the number of people either working or looking for work.
  a. The work force is 90 million. How many people are unemployed?

  b. What is the work force if 4,064,040 people are looking for work?

61. You bought a new car a year ago for $5,800. It is now worth only $4,500.
  a. What percent of the original cost is the car now worth?

  b. What percent of the original cost has the car decreased in value?

62. There are 65,847 voters registered in the Corbett School District. At a recent school board election,
  a. only about 12.1% of the voters voted. About how many people voted?

  b. only 4,401 people voted. To the nearest tenth, what percent of the registered voters was this?

63. A sweater which sold for $15 is now on sale for $11.25. What percent discount is being given?

64. You bought some stock a year ago for $5,000. By what percent has the value decreased if the stock is now worth
  a. $4,900?

  b. $2,500?

  c. $3,000?

65. What percent of a pound is

a. 4 ounces?

b. 10 ounces?

c. 24 ounces?

66. A jetliner carries 25% more fuel than is needed.

a–b. How long can the plane fly before running out of fuel if the flight normally takes

a. 4 hours?

b. 6 hours 40 minutes?

c–d. How long does the flight normally take if the plane has enough fuel to fly

c. 6 hours?

d. 4 hours 10 minutes?

67. Mr. Jeffers was late getting to work a total of $6\frac{1}{2}$ hours last week. He was not allowed to make up the time lost. He was supposed to work 40 hours.

a. What percent of last week's time did he lose by being late?

b. He gets $8 an hour. How much money did he lose by being late?

68. How much is $\frac{2}{5}$ of 70% of 300?

69. A research laboratory reports a 65% success rate with a new method.

a. The method has been used 80 times. How many times has it failed?

b. The method has succeeded 78 times. How many times has it been used?

c. The method failed 224 times. How many times has it been used?

d. The method has succeeded 468 times. How many times has it failed?

e. The method has failed 126 times. How many times has it succeeded?

70. At a certain company, 12% of the workers are usually absent, and 150 people work at this company.

a. How many workers are usually absent on a working day?

b. Suppose the same amount of work is to get done as when everyone is working. By what percent is the workload of the remaining workers increased?

71. A 6-year savings certificate earns $7\frac{1}{2}$% annual interest. How much interest will be earned over the life of the certificate if

a. \$1,000 is invested?

b. \$7,000 is invested?

c. \$5,500 is invested?

72. For filing Form A (a tax form) late, the penalty is 5% for each 30 days (or part thereof). But the penalty cannot go over 25%. Goofers filed Form A late. There was \$520 tax due on it. How much money was due for the penalty if Goofers filed the form

a. 30 days late?

b. 45 days late?

c. 90 days late?

d. 210 days late?

73. The owner of a hardware store bought some pipe fittings for $3.50 each and sold them for $5 each.

a. What percent of the selling price was the cost?

b. What percent of the selling price was the profit?

c. What percent of the cost was the selling price?

d. What percent of the cost was the profit?

74. A savings account earns 5% annual interest compounded quarterly. Ms. King put $3,000 in a savings account on April 1st. Each time interest was earned, she left it in the account. She did not add or take out any other amounts.

a. How much was in the account on July 1st?

b. How much was in the account on October 1st?

c. How much was in the account on the following April 1st?

75. A candy store owner wants to sell a mixture of two kinds of candies. The first kind sells for $2 a pound. The second kind sells for $3 a pound. How much should the mixture sell for if it is made of

a. 50% of each kind?

b. 40% of the first kind and 60% of the second kind?

c. 20% of the first kind and 80% of the second kind?

d. 80% of the first kind and 20% of the second kind?

76. A credit card company charges an annual interest rate of 18% on the average unpaid balance. The interest charge is wiped out if the cardholder pays the bill by the due date.

a. What percent is the monthly interest?

b. The Crilons' average unpaid balance last month was $322. How much extra will they have to pay if they are late in paying the bill?

c. In item b above, suppose the Crilons paid all but $10 by the due date. How much will the interest charge be?

77. An antiques dealer bought a chair for $500. She sold it for $800. What percent of the selling price was
   a. the profit?

   b. the cost?

78. A savings account in your bank pays 5% annual interest compounded quarterly. A savings account in your credit union pays 6% annual interest compounded quarterly. You have $6,000 to invest. Interest is rounded to the nearest cent.
   a. Make a schedule like the one below and fill it in.

End of Quarter Number	BANK		CREDIT UNION	
	Quarterly Interest	Balance	Quarterly Interest	Balance
0	0	$6000.00	0	$6000.00
1				
2				
3				
4				
5				
6				
7				
8				

   b. At which place will you have a higher balance at the end of two years, and how much higher will it be?

79. The average American male is 5 feet 10 inches tall. Mr. Harper is 5 feet 11 inches tall. By what percent is Mr. Harper taller than the average American male?

80. How much is $85\frac{7}{8}\% - \frac{3}{4}$?

81. A sewing supplies store bought a bolt of material for $1.50 a meter and sold it for $2.25 a meter.

a. What percent of the selling price was the cost?

b. What percent of the selling price was the profit?

c. What percent of the cost was the selling price?

d. What percent of the cost was the profit?

82. A department store salesperson gets a base salary of $120 a week. Besides this, he gets 2% of all the sales he makes. How much did he make last week if his sales were

a. $537?

b. $4,887.50?

83. Refer again to problem 82 above. How much were the salesperson's sales last week if he made

a. $171.75?

b. $415.79?

84. **a.** Big Corporation stock sold yesterday for $70 a share. Today it is $80 a share. By what percent did the price increase?

b. Big Corporation stock sold yesterday for $80 a share. Today it is $70 a share. By what percent did the price decrease?

85. For filing Form B (a tax form) late, the penalty is 5% for each month (or part thereof). The penalty does not go over 25%. Besides the penalty, interest of $\frac{1}{2}$% a month (or part thereof) is charged. Bumblers filed Form B late. There was $3,879.45 due on it.

a–c. How much money was due for penalties if Bumblers filed Form B

a. $1\frac{1}{2}$ months late?

b. 5 months late?

c. 7 months late?

d–f. How much money was due for interest if Bumblers filed Form B

d. $1\frac{1}{2}$ months late?

e. 5 months late?

f. 7 months late?

g–i. How much money was due for penalties and interest if Bumblers filed Form B

g. $1\frac{1}{2}$ months late?

h. 5 months late?

i. 7 months late?

86. A gallon is what percent of

a. 1 quart?

b. 2 quarts?

c. 9 quarts?

87. You work as a car salesperson. You get a commission of 3% of the selling price. On the average, a car sells for $6,140. On this basis, how many cars do you have to sell

a. in a week to make at least $450 that week?

b. in a year to average at least $450 a week?

88. Five years ago a home computer cost $990. Now the cost of such a computer is $550.

a. What percent of the old cost is the cost now?

b. By what percent did the cost of a home computer decrease?

c. What percent of today's cost was the old cost?

d. By what percent was the old cost higher than today's cost?

89. Mark scored 80% on a test.

a. The test had 25 problems on it. How many problems did Mark have wrong?

b. Mark had 16 problems right. How many problems were on the test?

c. Mark had 12 problems wrong. How many problems were on the test?

90. At Corbett High School, 45% of the students take business courses.

a. Corbett has 1,120 students. How many take business courses?

b. At Corbett, 783 students take business courses. How many students does Corbett have?

91. A 4-year savings certificate earns 7% annual interest. A 6-year savings certificate earns 7% annual interest. You have $5,000 to invest. How much more a year will the interest be on the 6-year certificate than on the 4-year certificate?

92. What percent of one week is

a. 1 day?

b. 3 days?

c. 6 days?

93. A survey last week showed that 47.1% of the people interviewed said they watch TV every day. Another 42.7% said they watch TV only about 3 or 4 times a week. And 15.2% said they watch TV only once a week or less. What's wrong with these results?

94. A certain kind of candy is 63% sugar.

a–b. You bought 5 pounds of the candy. Answer to the nearest tenth.

a. How many pounds are sugar?

b. How many ounces are sugar?

c–d. Of the candy you bought, 5 pounds is sugar. Answer to the nearest tenth.

c. How many pounds of candy did you buy?

d. How many ounces of candy did you buy?

95. A chemical is made up of six different ingredients. It contains 5 grams of A, 1.5 grams of B, 2 grams of C, 11.5 grams of D, 3.25 grams of E, and 1.75 grams of F. What percent of the mixture is

a. A?

b. B?

c. C?

d. D?

e. E?

f. F?

96. Hamburger contains 26% fat. You buy 5 pounds of hamburger. When you cook it, how much of it

a. will fry away as melted fat?

b. will be left as meat to eat?

CHAPTER 7
MIXED CONCEPTS 1

INSTRUCTIONS

A. No problem is meant to trick you.

Example

Problem: You buy meat for $3.87. You give the cashier $5. How much change do you get?

Answer: $1.13 (Assume you pay the full price for the meat. Assume you don't buy anything else. Assume there is no sales tax. Assume the cashier gives you the correct change.)

B. You are given all the information you need to solve each problem.

Example

Problem: Oranges sell for 90¢ a dozen. You buy 8 oranges. You give the cashier 75¢. How much change do you get?

Answer: 15¢ (Assume you can buy part of a dozen at the price of 90¢ a dozen. Assume you don't buy anything else. Assume the cashier charges you the right amount. Assume the cashier gives you the right amount of change.)

C. If the answer is a fraction, write it in reduced form.

Example

Problem: Forty people shared 10 pies. How much did each person get?

Answer: $\frac{1}{4}$ pie (We get an answer of $\frac{10}{40}$ pie, which we reduce to $\frac{1}{4}$ pie.)

D. Do not round off any answer unless the problem makes it right to do so.

Example

Problem: Peas sell at 3 cans for $1.01. You buy one can of peas. How much will you be charged?

Answer: $.34 or 34¢ (You can't pay a store a fractional part of one cent.)

E. Assume that a business will always round a part of a cent up, not down, when you are to pay.

Example

Problem: Peas sell at 3 cans for $1. You buy one can of peas. How much will you be charged?

Answer: $.34 or 34¢ (not $.33 or 33¢—Also, you can't pay a store a fractional part of one cent.)

F. If an answer is not about money and if the problem does not tell you how many decimal places to use, then carry the division to two decimal places unless you have a zero remainder before then.

Example

Problem: Write $\frac{49}{16}$ as a decimal.

Answer: $3.06\frac{1}{4}$ (not $3\frac{1}{16}$, not $3.0\frac{5}{8}$, not $3.062\frac{1}{2}$, and not 3.0625)

G. In general, if a percent is not a whole number, write the remainder as a fraction, not as a decimal.

Example

Problem: Rawlins earned $20,000 last year. This year she will earn $24,000. What percent of this year's earnings were last year's earnings?

Answer: $83\frac{1}{3}$ % (not 83.3% or 83.33% or 83.333%, etc.)

1. Jan watched 5 TV programs every day for a week. These were the only TV programs she watched. How many TV programs did she watch that week?

2. A large cake was cut into 24 pieces. Each piece was the same size. The cake was shared equally by 8 people. How many pieces did each person get?

3. George, Scott, Sue, Jane, and Charo each wrote a theme for English class. George's theme had 135 words. Scott's had 122 words. Sue's had 113 words. Jane's had 110 words. Charo's had 145 words. What was the total number of words on the five themes?

4. A pet shop has 6 different kinds of kittens. It has 4 kittens of each kind. How many kittens does it have?

5. There are 20 short blocks in a mile. Joy lives 30 short blocks from school. How many miles does Joy live from school?

6. A heavy truck had 6 axles. Five axles each had 4 wheels. The other axle had 2 wheels. What was the total number of wheels the truck had?

7. A school district has two junior high schools. One of these has 536 students. The other has 638 students. What is the total number of students in the junior high schools?

8. A bus started out with only the driver on it. At the first stop, 7 people got on the bus. At the second stop, 2 people got on. At the third stop, 3 people got on and 2 got off. How many people were left on the bus?

9. Mr. Barker works 9 miles from his home. He drives back and forth each day. He works 5 days a week. How far does he drive going back and forth to work each week?

10. Black pencils cost 10¢ each. Red pencils cost 5¢ each. How much does it cost for 2 black pencils and 1 red pencil?

11. A newspaper has 10 comic strips on a page. Each comic strip has 4 pictures. How many comic strip pictures are on the page?

12. A jet flight from Detroit to Los Angeles is 1969 miles. The flight from Los Angeles to San Diego is 109 miles. A passenger gets on at Detroit and gets off at San Diego, but the plane stops first in Los Angeles. How far does the passenger travel?

13. A TV movie was interrupted 5 times each hour for commercials. Four commercials were shown during each interruption. The movie started at 8:00 P.M. and ended at 11:00 P.M. How many commercials were shown during the interruptions?

14. Ace Tallguy is a basketball player. In 5 games, he scored 24, 35, 30, 27, and 34 points. What was the average number of points he scored per game?

15. In another five games, Ace Tallguy scored a total of 170 points. What was the average number of points he scored per game?

16. Jose bought 6 candy bars. Each candy bar weighed 170 grams. What was the total weight of the 6 candy bars?

17. Mr. Black teaches 4 different groups of students. One group has 25 students. Another group has 36 students. Another group has 14 students. The last group has 27 students. How many students are there altogether in the 4 groups?

18. Pop costs 20¢ a bottle. How much do 6 bottles of pop cost?

19. Bob, Joyce, and Mark each have 5 pairs of slacks. What is the total number of pairs of slacks they have?

20. In a baseball diamond, there are 90 feet between bases. How far is it all the way around?

21. A toothpaste test was conducted on 5 groups of 75 people each. How many people were in the test?

22. There were 44 problems on a test Tom took. He missed $\frac{1}{4}$ of them. How many problems did he miss?

23. There were 48 problems on a test Debby took. She missed 25% of them. How many problems did Debby get right?

24. An airliner has 50 rows of seats. Each row has 3 seats on one side, 4 seats in the middle, and 2 seats on the other side. How many seats are in the 50 rows?

25. There are 12 inches in a foot. There are 5280 feet in a mile. How many inches are there in a mile?

26. There are 100 yards between end zones on a football field. How many feet is this?

27. Jake goes to the store. His purchases total $1.29. He gives the cashier $2.00. How much change should he get?

28. Scott's salary is $130 a week. The payroll office withholds $25 for federal income tax, $6.50 for state income tax, and $8.00 for social security tax. What is Scott's net pay each week?

29. The gas tank of your car holds 21 gallons. It is $\frac{1}{3}$ full. How many gallons will it take to fill the tank?

30. Mary earns $4.15 an hour. How much does she earn if she works 35 hours?

31. Emma had scores of 85%, 90%, 70%, and 95% on four tests. What was her average score for these tests?

32. Cass went to the supermarket. He bought bread for 52¢, hamburger for $1.65, and cheese for 93¢. What was the total?

33. Truck tires cost $68 each. The truck has 14 wheels. How much will it cost to buy tires for all the wheels of the truck?

34. Mrs. Corey gets a bill for $50. The bill says she will get a 15% discount if she pays within 10 days. How much will she save if she pays the bill within 10 days?

35. An ad was run on three TV stations. In one night, it was shown 6 times on one station, 3 times on another, and 9 times on the third. What was the total number of times it was shown on the three stations that night?

36. Gasoline costs 79.8¢ a gallon. How much do 15 gallons of gasoline cost?

37. Bread is on sale at 3 loaves for $1.00.

a. How much will 6 loaves of bread cost?

b. You buy 3 loaves. What is the average cost of each loaf?

c. You buy 1 loaf. How much will you be charged?

38. You buy a hamburger for 75¢, a milk shake for 45¢, and french fries for 35¢. What is your total bill?

39. A road map shows a scale of 1 cm = 26 km. You want to drive to a city which is $2\frac{1}{2}$ cm away on the map. How many kilometers away is the city?

40. Bob types an average of 65 words a minute. How many words does he type in 8 minutes?

41. A recipe for a batch of fudge calls for $\frac{3}{4}$ cup of cocoa. How much cocoa should be used for a double batch of fudge?

42. Yancy's car used 24 liters of gasoline for a trip of 300 kilometers. On the average, how many kilometers did the car go for each liter of gasoline used?

43. Mrs. Blue paid $225 for a sofa. When it was delivered, she found a flaw. The store gave her a refund of $30. How much did the sofa cost her?

44. Imported cheese costs $1.70 for a half pound. How much will 2 pounds of the cheese cost?

45. A plane would fly at 700 kilometers an hour if there were no head wind (wind blowing against the plane's direction of travel). How fast will it fly if the head wind is 100 kilometers an hour?

46. Otis telephoned Judy. Judy's phone rang twice. It was 5 seconds from the start of the first ring to the start of the second ring. The phone rang for 1 second each time. How long was the phone silent between the two rings?

47. There are 35 cows and 24 birds standing in a field. All are typical animals. How many legs do they have (total)?

48. Two movies were shown one right after the other. The first one lasted 1 hour and 40 minutes. The second one lasted 2 hours and 35 minutes. How long did it take to show the two movies?

49. A package of cookies contains 26 cookies. Betty wants to have an average of 4 cookies for each of 20 guests. How many packages of cookies should she buy?

50. Two cats each had 5 kittens. Each of the kittens later had 4 kittens. What was the total number of the kittens' kittens?

51. Lila typed 720 words in 12 minutes. What was her average number of words a minute?

52. A jetliner traveling from New York City to Los Angeles flew at an altitude of 35,000 feet. How many miles high (to the nearest tenth) did it fly?

53. The area of a room is 24 square meters. How many square centimeters is this?

54. The usual price on a CD you want is $11.70. It will be on sale next week for $\frac{1}{3}$ off. How much will you save if you wait until next week to buy the CD?

55. Mr. Dakker wants to plant alyssum seeds along a 40-foot border of his lawn. He figures that each package of seeds will cover 5 feet. How many packages of seeds should he buy?

56. A farmer sells two hogs at 20¢ a pound. One hog weighs 465 pounds. The other weighs 375 pounds. How much does the farmer get, in all, for the two hogs?

57. The Nile River in Africa is the longest river in the world. It has a length of 4132 miles. The Ob-Irtysh River is the longest river in Asia. It has a length of 3461 miles. How much longer is the Nile River than the Ob-Irtysh River?

58. To make coffee, Mr. Jackson uses $\frac{3}{4}$ of a tablespoon of coffee for each cup. He uses another tablespoon of coffee "for the pot." How many tablespoons of coffee will he use if he makes 10 cups of coffee in the pot at one time?

59. You buy a suit for $60 plus 4% sales tax. What is the total amount that you pay?

60. A car travels 200 kilometers in $2\frac{1}{2}$ hours. What ... average speed?

61. There are about 2,000 factories in the Baltimore area. These factories make about $3 billion in goods yearly. What is the average value of the goods made yearly by each of these factories?

62. A car travels at an average speed of 60 kph for $3\frac{3}{4}$ hours. How far does it travel in this time?

63. Each day for a year Joe ate 3 meals and 4 snacks. What was the total number of meals and snacks Joe ate that year?

64. You make $3.76 an hour when you work. You work $23\frac{1}{2}$ hours one week. How much do you make that week?

65. Rose went to the Post Office. She bought eleven 15¢ stamps, four 12¢ stamps, and six 20¢ stamps. What was the total she paid for the stamps?

66. You have a sheet of paper. You tear it in half. You stack the pieces and then tear the stack in half. Again you stack the pieces and tear the stack in half. How many pieces of paper do you have now?

67. Ms. Worth is an attorney. She charges $70 an hour for consultation. What is her charge to a client who consulted with her for 4 hours?

68. The college bookstore sold 75 books today for a total of $688.50. What was the average selling price of each book?

69. Mount Everest in Asia is the highest mountain in the world. It is 29,028 feet high. The highest mountain in North America is Mount McKinley (Denali) in Alaska. Its height is 20,320 feet. How much higher is Mount Everest than Mount McKinley?

70. Each roll of candy contains 20 pieces of candy. How many pieces of candy are in 19 rolls?

71. Oranges sell at $1.75 a dozen. If you buy a dozen at a time, what is the average price of an orange?

72. The year before last Kim was 122 cm tall. Last year she was 126 cm tall. This year she is 132 cm tall. How much taller is Kim now than she was two years ago?

73. Gasoline sells for 20.2¢ a liter. How much will 55 liters cost?

74. A store is having a 1¢ sale on pencils. The regular price of a pencil is 15¢. For every pencil Jerry buys at the regular price, he can buy another one for only 1¢.

a. How much will Jerry have to pay if he buys 15 pencils?

b. How much will Jerry have to pay if he buys 16 pencils?

75. A standard badminton court is 20 feet wide and 44 feet long. What is its area?

76. On May 4, 1961, two U.S. Navy men rose to 113,739.9 feet in a balloon. To the nearest tenth, how many miles high was this?

77. At birth, a baby's head is about $\frac{1}{4}$ the length of the rest of its body. A newborn baby's total length is 50 cm.

a. How long is its head?

b. How long is the rest of its body?

78. An average baby weighs about 3 kilograms at birth. It will double its birth weight within six months and will triple it in about a year. How much will an average baby weigh at the end of

a. Six months?

b. About a year?

79. A shop class has 10 girls and 15 boys. What percent of the class is girls?

80. The city of Triticum produces more flour yearly than any other city in the United States. There are 24 grain elevators in Triticum. These elevators can store more than 70 million bushels of grain. On the average, how much grain can each Triticum elevator store?

81. The city of Oswald has about 450 plants which, combined, employ more than 60,000 people. What is the average number of people employed in an Oswald plant?

82. There are 2.54 centimeters in an inch. How many centimeters are there in 15 inches?

83. Four people chipped in equal amounts to buy a large pizza. The pizza cost $4.60.

a. How much did each person chip in?

b. The pizza was cut into 8 pieces. Each person ate 2 pieces. What was the average cost of a piece of pizza?

84. Not counting Alaska, the area of the continental United States is about 12 times the area of Burma. Burma's area is 678,033 square kilometers. About how big is the area of the continental United States, not including Alaska?

85. A printer uses a single sheet of paper to make 4 pages in a book. (Each sheet is folded in half and is printed on both sides of both halves.) How many sheets of paper does he need to make a 580-page book?

86. In the U.S., there are about 320,000 school buses which carry about 20,000,000 students back and forth to school each year. On the average, how many students does each bus carry?

87. Mr. Joyan stayed at a hotel in a state that has a tax of 8% on room rentals. The rental charge totaled $105, not including the tax. How much was the tax?

88. A centrifuge turns 6000 times a minute. How many times a second does it turn?

89. Gasoline sells for 19.6¢ a liter. How many liters (to the nearest tenth) can you buy for $12?

90. Kleland, a small country, has about 4,000,000 people. Only about 5% of the people can read and write. About how many people in Kleland cannot read and write?

91. The population of East Metropolis is about 1,087,450. The population of West Metropolis is about 2,136,500. What is the total population of Metropolis?

92. A typist bought some typing supplies. She paid $4.75 for a ream of paper. She paid $2.35 for a typewriter ribbon. She paid 20¢ for a typewriter eraser. Altogether, how much did she spend on these supplies?

93. A serving of peas weighs 75 grams. How many servings are in a 900-gram can of peas?

94. A particular city has about 745 industrial plants. These plants manufacture $540 million in goods annually. To the nearest cent, what is the average value of the goods manufactured by a plant in this city?

95. There are 6 telephone cables across the Atlantic Ocean. Each can carry 138 conversations at once. How many telephone conversations can the 6 cables handle all at once?

96. The Panama Canal was completed in 1914 at a cost of about $380 million. It is about 81.6 kilometers long. What was the average cost per kilometer?

97. There are 13 islands in the Canary Islands, but only 7 are inhabited. What percent are inhabited?

98. The 13 Canary Islands have a total area of 7273 square kilometers. On the average, what is the area of one of the Canary Islands?

99. The 7 populated Canary Islands have a total of about 1,200,000 people. On the average, about how many people live on each of these 7 islands?

100. The wax of the berries of the candleberry shrub is used for making candles. A bushel of berries yields about 2 kilograms of wax. How many bushels of berries would be needed to yield about 75 kilograms of wax?

101. A rectangle is 20 cm by 30 cm. There is a border all around it which is 4 cm wide. What are the dimensions of the rectangle and the border together?

102. In 1861, the population of Chattanooga, Tennessee, was 5545. In 1975, it was 119,923. By how much did Chattanooga's population increase from 1861 to 1975?

103. A circular swimming pool has a radius of 4 meters. What is its circumference? (Use $\pi = 3.1416$.)

104. Five monkeys climbed coconut trees and started throwing coconuts at each other. The first monkey threw 17 coconuts. The second threw 15. The third threw 20. The fourth threw 13. The fifth threw 25. What was the total number of coconuts thrown?

105. What's the difference (if any) between an area described as "4 kilometers square" and an area described as "4 square kilometers"?

106. Forests cover about 43% of California's 411,013 square kilometers. About how much area do these forests cover?

107. In 1974, Chemical & Engineering News reported figures for Exxon Corporation as follows: total sales, $25,724,000,000; chemical sales, $1,563,000,000. According to these figures,

a. how much more were Exxon's total sales than its chemical sales?

b. what percent of Exxon's total sales were its chemical sales?

108. Canada has about 23,000,000 people. About 76% of the people live in cities.

a. What percent of Canada's people do not live in cities?

b. How many people is this?

109. There are about 25 million books, pamphlets, and periodicals in 700 public libraries. Suppose that each of these libraries has the same number of books, etc. Then about how many books, etc. are in each library?

110. Small Country's population is estimated at 9,125,000. Its population density is $82\frac{1}{4}$ people per square kilometer. To the nearest whole number, what was the area of Small Country?

111. A math class of 27 students has 12 boys. What percent of the class is girls?

112. Tammy built a birdhouse for a robin. She made the floor 18 cm square. She made the house 19 cm high. What was the volume of the robin's house?

113. A map is drawn to a scale of 1 cm = 118 km. How many km apart are two towns which are $4\frac{1}{2}$ cm apart on this map?

114. In 1939, Berlin's population was about 4,340,000. In 1945, it was about 2,800,000. By how much did Berlin's population decrease in these six years?

115. Ms. Edding bought 6 dozen eggs for a total of $7.00. What was the average price of each egg?

116. Ms. Felding went golfing. Par on the front 9 holes was 68. Par on the back 9 holes was 67. Ms. Felding's score on the front 9 holes was 72. Her score on the back 9 holes was 70. Was her score over par or under par, and by how much was it over or under?

117. It took Ms. Jotwin 5 hours to drive her car 350 km. What was the car's average speed during this time?

118. Mr. Atkins drove his car for 4 hours at an average speed of 80 kph. How far did his car go in this time?

119. Isaac went to a school carnival. He bought 5 tickets at 10¢ each, 4 tickets at 25¢ each, and 10 tickets at 5¢ each. What was the total cost of the tickets he bought?

120. The cost of a pony ride at the school carnival was 50¢. At the end of the carnival, the total amount collected for pony rides was $153.50. No one had a free pony ride. How many pony rides were there?

121. The school carnival also had a "car smash." For 25¢, a person could smash at the car three times with a sledgehammer. The "car smash" collected a total of $109.75. No one hit the car without paying. Everyone who paid hit the car exactly three times.

a. How many people hit the car?

b. How many times was the car hit?

122. Ms. Sims is a mail delivery person. She walks an average of 11 miles a day on her job. She works an average of 220 days a year. What is the average number of miles Ms. Sims walks on her job in a year?

123. Ms. Wilson ran two want ads in the local newspaper. The cost of one ad was $4.65. The cost of the other ad was $3.15. What was the total cost of the two ads?

124. Mr. Jackson bought a used van for $1500. He gave a deposit of $250. How much did he still owe?

125. Suki's school collected 15,000 pounds of paper during a paper drive. The paper company paid $1.45 for each 100 pounds of paper. How much money did the school get for the paper collected?

126. A restaurant has a special lunch. The lunch sells for $3 for an adult's portion and $2 for a child's portion. How much will the restaurant charge for 11 adults' portions and 15 children's portions?

127. Hamburger contains 28% fat. You buy 10 kilograms of hamburger. All the fat cooks away when you fry the hamburger. How many kilograms of meat will you have after you fry the hamburger?

128. A $\frac{1}{4}$-grain tablet of saccharin has the sweetening power of 1 teaspoonful of sugar. How much sweetening power does a 1-grain tablet of saccharin have?

129. Ms. Brooks bought 40 liters of gasoline at 17.1¢ a liter. She also bought 4 liters of oil at $1.33 a liter. How much did she spend in all?

130. A filing clerk filed 15 cards under "A." He filed 11 cards under "C." He filed 25 cards under "M." He filed 3 cards under "Y." He did not file any other cards. What was the total number of cards he filed?

131. A hummingbird egg is about 13 mm long. An ostrich egg is about 15 cm long. What percent of the length of an ostrich egg is the length of a hummingbird egg?

132. The average weight of an elephant's brain is 5000 grams. The average weight of a man's brain is 1400 grams. What percent of the average weight of an elephant's brain is the average weight of a man's brain?

133. When you eat at a restaurant, it is usual to tip the waiter or waitress 15% of the meal charge. Edith ate at a restaurant yesterday. Her meal charge was $3.60. She also left the usual tip. How much was the tip she left?

134. Four years ago Kyle's salary was $6,500. Three years ago it was $7,500. Two years ago it was $11,000. Last year it was $14,000. This year Kyle's salary will be $17,000. What is Kyle's average salary over these years?

135. California has 5 state-supported colleges and 14 state-supported universities. About 300,000 students are enrolled in these. On the average, how many students are enrolled at each of these colleges and universities?

136. A rectangle has a width of $3\frac{1}{2}$ feet and a length of $5\frac{1}{4}$ feet. What is the distance all the way around it?

CHAPTER 8

MIXED CONCEPTS 2

INSTRUCTIONS

A. No problem is meant to trick you.

Example

Problem: You buy meat for $3.87. You give the cashier $5. How much change do you get?

Answer: $1.13 (Assume you pay the full price for the meat. Assume you don't buy anything else. Assume there is no sales tax. Assume the cashier gives you the correct change.)

B. You are given all the information you need to solve each problem.

Example

Problem: Oranges sell for 90¢ a dozen. You buy 8 oranges. You give the cashier 75¢. How much change do you get?

Answer: 15¢ (Assume you can buy part of a dozen at the price of 90¢ a dozen. Assume you don't buy anything else. Assume the cashier charges you the right amount. Assume the cashier gives you the right amount of change.)

C. If the answer is a fraction, write it in reduced form.

Example

Problem: Forty people shared 10 pies. How much did each person get?

Answer: $\frac{1}{4}$ pie (We get an answer of $\frac{10}{40}$ pie, which we reduce to $\frac{1}{4}$ pie.)

D. Do not round off any answer unless the problem makes it right to do so.

Example

Problem: Peas sell at 3 cans for $1.01. You buy one can of peas. How much will you be charged?

Answer: $.34 or 34¢ (You can't pay a store a fractional part of one cent.)

E. Assume that a business will always round a part of a cent up, not down, when you are to pay.

Example

Problem: Peas sell at 3 cans for $1. You buy one can of peas. How much will you be charged?

Answer: $.34 or 34¢ (not $.33 or 33¢—Also, you can't pay a store a fractional part of one cent.)

F. If an answer is not about money, and if the problem does not tell you how many decimal places to use, then carry the division to two decimal places unless you have a zero remainder before then.

Example

Problem: Write $\frac{49}{16}$ as a decimal.

Answer: $3.06\frac{1}{4}$ (not $3\frac{1}{16}$, not $3.0\frac{5}{8}$, not $3.062\frac{1}{2}$, and not 3.0625)

G. In general, if a percent is not a whole number, write the remainder as a fraction, not as a decimal.

Example

Problem: Rawlins earned $20,000 last year. This year she will earn $24,000. What percent of this year's earnings were last year's earnings?

Answer: $83\frac{1}{3}$% (not 83.3% or 83.33% or 83.333%, etc.)

1. Your car's gas tank holds 100 liters of gasoline. You fill the tank. You drive 400 kilometers. It takes 80 liters to fill the tank again. How far did your car go for each liter of gasoline used?

2. Marguerita bought 3 blouses for a total of $15.50. She found a flaw in one later and returned it to the store. The store gave her a full refund, $4.74. What was the average price of the blouses she kept?

3. A supermarket's cost of groceries averages 86% of the selling price. One day the market sells a total of $4187.60 in groceries. How much profit did the market make on the groceries that day?

4. The yearly finance charge on a used car is 16% of the original unpaid balance. You buy the car for $5000. You pay $1000 down (no trade-in). You agree to pay off the car over a three-year period. What will the total finance charge be?

5. A room without windows is 12 feet wide and 16 feet long. The ceiling is 8 feet high. What is the wall area of the room, including doorways?

6. You make $5.62 an hour. You work 40 hours one week. The payroll office takes the following amounts from your pay: 18% for federal income tax; 5% for state income tax; 6.1% for social security tax; 1% for union dues. Give the amount of each of the following: gross pay, federal income tax, state income tax, social security tax, union dues, net pay.

7. Roy wants to invite 7 friends to his house. He wants to serve them hamburgers. He figures he can make 5 hamburgers from each pound. He figures he and his friends will each eat 4 hamburgers. Hamburger costs $1.15 a pound.
   a. How many pounds should he buy?

   b. How much will it cost?

8. To figure typing speed (in words a minute), count the total number of characters typed (including spaces). Then divide by five. And then divide by the number of minutes typed. Randy typed 1500 characters in 6 minutes. What was his typing speed?

9. Bank A pays 3/4% more in yearly interest than Bank B. How much more interest will $5000 earn in a year in Bank A than in Bank B?

10. Bacteria are found almost everywhere. It is thought that the air may have more than 100 bacteria in each cubic foot. If so, how many bacteria might there be in a school room 20 feet wide by 30 feet long if the ceiling is 12 feet high?

11. A picture is 42 cm long and 32 cm wide. It has a 5 cm wide frame around it. All around the picture, 1 cm of the picture sticks into the frame so that the frame can hold it. What is the area of the frame?

12. There are 330 people in one company and 250 people in another company. The two companies got together to form a bowling league. One sixth of the people from the first company joined the league. From the second company, 10% joined the league. How many people were in the bowling league?

13. Ms. Wemming is going to buy a refrigerator. The price is $375 if she pays cash. If she makes monthly payments, she must pay $80 down and then pay $28.27 a month for 12 months. Which way of paying will cost her less? How much less?

14. On a series of plays, the Detroit Lions gained 9 yards on a first down, lost 3 yards on the second down, gained a yard on the third down, and gained 5 yards on the fourth down. On the next series of plays, they gained 4 yards on the first down, gained 2 more on the second down, lost 3 yards on the third down, and gained 5 yards on the fourth down. What was their average gain per down on these two series of plays?

15. Two brands of tomatoes are of equal quality. One brand sells at three 400-gram cans for 79¢, and the second brand sells at two 650-gram cans for 87¢. Which brand is the better buy?

16. A state law says a minor may not spend more than 48 hours a week going to school and working. Martha attends school from 7:45 A.M. to 1:15 P.M. each day Monday through Friday. She also works afternoons at a restaurant. What is the maximum number of hours the state law allows Martha to work in a week (during the school year, not counting vacations)?

17. Mr. Johnson's salary is $270 a week. How much is his monthly salary?

18. Mr. Jones wants to paint the walls in three rooms white. In one room, the wall area is 336 square feet. In another room, the wall area is 400 square feet. The wall area of the third room is 364 square feet. A gallon of paint covers 300 square feet. How many gallons of paint should Mr. Jones buy to do the job? (Assume that partial gallons of paint are not sold.)

19. In Ms. Doan's class, 40% of the class are boys; 60% of Mr. Fry's class are boys. There are 25 students in Ms. Doan's class and 30 students in Mr. Fry's class. No boy is in both classes. How many boys are in these classes?

20. Marinda bought six bottles of pop for a total of $2.50, including bottle deposits totaling $1.20. What was the average price of each bottle of pop, not including the bottle deposit?

21. A pound of gold contains 12 ounces (apothecaries' weight or troy weight). A pound of feathers contains 16 ounces (avoirdupois weight or U.S. customary system). Given the different systems of measurement, which is heavier—6 pounds of gold or 12 pounds of feathers if

a. an ounce in either system weighs the same amount?

b. an ounce in apothecaries' weight is heavier than an ounce in avoirdupois weight?

22. The charges for running a 15-second ad on a TV station are as follows:

$200 from 12:00 A.M. to 6:30 A.M.
$300 from 6:30 A.M. to 9:00 A.M.
$350 from 9:00 A.M. to 11:00 A.M.
$400 from 11:00 A.M. to 3:30 P.M.
$450 from 3:30 P.M. to 6:00 P.M.
$500 from 6:00 P.M. to 8:00 P.M.
$600 from 8:00 P.M. to 11:00 P.M.
$500 from 11:00 P.M. to 11:30 P.M.
$400 from 11:30 P.M. to 12:00 A.M.

a. Big Corporation runs 15-second ads on the station as follows:

3 ads from 9:00 A.M. to 11:00 A.M.
5 ads from 11:00 A.M. to 2:00 P.M.
6 ads from 8:00 P.M. to 11:00 P.M.

How much does Big Corporation owe the station for these ads for one day?

b. Hit Records runs 15-second ads on the station as follows:

15 ads from 12:00 A.M. to 6:30 A.M.
5 ads from 6:30 A.M. to 9:00 A.M.

How much does Hit Records owe the station for these ads for one day?

23. Jay worked one day from 9:12 A.M. to 3:45 P.M. How long did he work that day?

24. Jenny worked one day from 9:45 A.M. to 3:12 P.M. How long did she work that day?

25. In the two problems above, who worked longer (Jay or Jenny?), and how much longer did he or she work?

26. A barber charges $6.25 for a haircut and $3.50 for a shave. Last Tuesday, he shaved 19 customers and cut the hair of 21 customers. What was the total amount he charged for these services?

27. Art decided to walk in the March of Dimes Walkathon. He had a total of 53 sponsors, and 28 of them each pledged 10¢ a mile. The other sponsors each pledged 25¢ a mile. Art walked 20 miles in the Walkathon. How much (total) should he collect from his sponsors?

28. In 1975, the population of Brazil was estimated at about 107,702,000. It was also estimated that about $\frac{3}{4}$ of the people lived along the Atlantic coast in a strip 480 kilometers wide. Also, about 62% of the total population was urban, and about 38% was rural.

a. About how many Brazilians lived within the Atlantic coast strip?

b. About how many Brazilians lived in cities?

c. About how many Brazilians lived in rural areas?

29. A man owns two hotels. One has 436 rooms. The other has 362 rooms. On an average day, $\frac{2}{3}$ of the rooms are occupied.

a. What is the total number of rooms occupied in this man's hotels on an average day?

b. What is the total number of rooms unoccupied in this man's hotels on an average day?

30. In baseball, a player's batting average is figured by dividing the number of hits by the number of times at bat. A sacrifice is not counted as a time at bat. Tiger Walton has batted 33 times so far this season. He struck out 3 times, sacrificed 4 times, hit 3 flies caught by fielders, grounded out 14 times, hit 15 foul balls, hit 3 home runs, hit 2 doubles, and hit singles the other times. To three decimal places, what is his batting average so far this season?

31. In a war battle, an Army battalion, 880 people, was made up of four companies. Each company was made up of five platoons. Each platoon contained four squads. Each company had the same number of people, as did each platoon and each squad. How many people were in each squad?

32. Suppose that each squad in the army contains 12 people. A platoon contains 5 squads. A company contains 6 platoons. A battalion contains 3 companies. A brigade contains 4 battalions. How many people are in a brigade?

33. You buy a dozen oranges at 3 for 47¢. You also buy $1\frac{1}{2}$ pounds of potatoes at 26¢ a pound. What is your total bill for these items?

34. Two salesmen were competing for a prize. The prize was to go to whoever had the most sales in a week. Following is the record of their sales for the week.

Day	Salesman 1	Salesman 2
1	$1,056.27	none
2	537.65	$956.78
3	784.97	877.60
4	422.11	none
5	217.85	988.90
6	335.22	869.70
7	325.90	none

a. What was the total of the sales by salesman 1?

b. What was the total of the sales by salesman 2?

c. Who won the contest?

35. A room measures 4 meters by $5\frac{1}{2}$ meters. What is its area in square centimeters?

36. Gold jewelry is not usually pure gold but is an alloy of gold and other metals. One carat of gold means that $\frac{1}{24}$ of the total weight of the alloy is gold.

a. A ring is 14-carat gold. What fraction of the alloy in the ring is gold?

b. A watch case is 10-carat gold. What percent of the alloy in the watch case is gold?

37. A discount movie theater charges $2.50 for an adult's ticket. It charges $1.75 for a child's ticket. How much will the theater collect if it sells 115 adults' tickets and 198 children's tickets?

38. Peas sell for 2 cans for 55¢. The selling price of a 24-can case of peas is $6.20. Mr. Whitney and Ms. Janning both used 24 cans of peas over a 4-month period. Mr. Whitney bought them 2 at a time. Ms. Janning bought a case. Who paid more, and how much more?

39. The Standard Oil Building in Chicago is 1136 feet tall and has 80 stories. The John Hancock Center in Chicago is 1107 feet tall and has 100 stories.

a. What is the average number of feet per story (to the nearest hundredth) of the Standard Oil Building?

b. What is the average number of feet per story (to the nearest hundredth) of the John Hancock Center?

c. To the nearest tenth, what percent of the Standard Oil Building's height is the John Hancock Center's height?

d. To the nearest tenth, what percent of the average story height of the Standard Oil Building is the average story height of the John Hancock Center?

e. Suppose that the average story height of the Standard Oil Building were the same as that of the John Hancock Center. How tall (to the nearest foot) would the Standard Oil Building be?

f. Suppose that the average story height of the John Hancock Center were the same as the average story height of the Standard Oil Building. How tall (to the nearest foot) would the John Hancock Center be?

40. A travel agency gets a 10% commission on each airline ticket it sells. It gets a 15% commission on each hotel reservation it makes (provided that the reservation is kept, of course). One month it sells a total of $5,724.80 in airline tickets and it makes hotel reservations totaling $2,435.00, all of which are kept. How much does it earn in commissions?

41. A house plan has a scale of $\frac{1}{4}$ inch = 1 foot. When a room 12 feet by 15 feet is drawn on this house plan, what will its house plan dimensions be?

42. The area of Ethiopia is 471,778 square miles or 1,221,000 square kilometers. The area of Tanzania is 364,900 square miles or 945,087 square kilometers.

a. Use the areas in square miles. What percent (to the nearest tenth) of Ethiopia's area is Tanzania's area?

b. Use the areas in square kilometers. What percent (to the nearest tenth) of Ethiopia's area is Tanzania's area?

43. A savings bank pays interest at the rate of 6% a year. Each quarter they compute the interest earned for that quarter and they add it to the balance. If you put $1,000 in the bank on December 31st and do not make any withdrawals or any more deposits, how much will you have as of the end of December 31st of the next year?

44. Mr. Harris rented a power rake for his yard. The charge was $5.00 for the first hour and $3.50 an hour (or any part of an hour) for each hour after the first hour. He checked the power rake out at 10:12 A.M. He checked it back in at 2:28 P.M. How much did he owe for the rental?

45. Becky likes two kinds of potato chips—Crunchies and Krispys. A 340-gram bag of Crunchies sells for 99¢. A 340-gram bag of Krispys sells for $1.10. The Krispys are never burned or broken up. About $\frac{1}{10}$ of the Crunchies are always burned or broken up, and Becky always ends up throwing this $\frac{1}{10}$ out. Which brand should she buy in order to get the most for her money?

46. Each year, about $1,750,000,000 of ore is mined in California. This is about 5% of the total yearly value of goods produced in California. About how much is California's total yearly value of goods produced?

47. Most high school basketball courts are 84 feet by 50 feet. Most college and professional basketball courts are 94 feet by 50 feet. The area of the usual high school basketball court is what percent (to the nearest tenth) of the area of the usual professional basketball court?

48. A car's gas tank holds 90 liters. You fill the tank when the car's odometer shows 23,092.4 (kilometers); the gas tank takes 70 liters. The next time gas is needed, it takes 60 liters to fill the tank, and the odometer shows 23,635.1. What is the average number of kilometers (to the nearest tenth) traveled for each liter of gas used?

49. Joy's age is 15 years 6 months. Frank's age is 14 years 7 months. Randall's age is 17 years 8 months. What is the average age of these three people?

50. A telephone company bills phone calls by distance in four ways: local, near zone, far zone, and long distance. A "near zone" dialed call costs 4.3¢ a minute. A "far zone" dialed call costs 7.9¢ a minute. Any part of a minute counts as a full minute. On both kinds of calls there is an added charge of 1.5¢ a call if operator assistance is required.

a. John asks the operator to dial a "near zone" number for him. When his party answers, they talk for 3 minutes 15 seconds. What is the charge for John's call?

b. Josita dials a call to the "far zone." When her friend answers, they talk for 15 minutes 25 seconds. What is the charge for Josita's call?

51. You work at your job for a weekly salary of $80 plus 3% commission on all the sales you make. You make sales of $9,000 one week. How much altogether do you earn that week at your job?

52. A honeybee flies at a speed of about 12 miles an hour. About how many feet does it fly in one second?

53. Aluminum comes from bauxite ore. In Jamaica, 1200 tons of bauxite ore were mined. Of this 1200 tons, 564 tons were aluminum, 42 tons were silica, 24 tons were titanium oxide, 264 tons were iron oxide, and the rest was water. Tell what percent of the ore was made up of each part named above.

54. An income tax schedule shows the following:

If your taxable income is at least	but less than	then your tax is
0	$2,000	14% of your taxable income
$2,000	$4,000	$280 + 18% of the excess over $2,000
$4,000	$6,000	$640 + 22% of the excess over $4,000

a. How much is the income tax on a taxable income of $500?

b. How much is the income tax on a taxable income of $2,300?

c. How much is the income tax on a taxable income of $5,800?

55. A cash register started out with $20 in bills and change. Sales totaled $1,027.35, of which $548.50 was for charge sales and the rest for cash sales. Money was taken out as follows: $368.50 to pay for expenses; $50 to put in the petty cash fund. Also, another $35 was put in because the register was running short of change, and the store collected $100 on old charge sales. How much cash should have been in the register at this point?

56. Beefsteak contains 18.7% protein and 17% fat. Suppose a beefsteak weighs 250 grams. How many grams will be

a. protein?

b. fat?

57. Suppose 15 people pick 12 bushels of oranges and divide them evenly among themselves. How many bushels does each person get?

58. The Carlsbad Caverns National Park in New Mexico became a national park in 1930. At that time, the area above ground was 700 acres. By the start of 1975, much more area had been added to the park, and the area above ground was 46,753 acres.
   a. By what percent did the area of the park increase from 1930 to 1975?

   b. What was the average percent of increase each year? (Do not include 1930 or 1975.)

59. A family spends $\frac{1}{4}$ of its total income for housing. Of the housing amount, 1/5 is spent for utilities. The total income is $21,000 a year. How much a year is spent for utilities?

60. At noon, a gas station's pumps showed that the station had sold 513 gallons of regular gas and 625 gallons of lead-free gas. Regular gas sold for 72.1¢ a gallon. Lead-free gas sold for 76.3¢ a gallon. How much were the total gas sales as of noon?

61. In the United States, about 1,000 bus companies operate more than 22,000 intercity buses. Each year, the buses travel about 1,600,000,000 kilometers and carry about 400,000,000 riders. What is the average number of

a. buses each bus company operates?

b. riders each bus company carries yearly?

c. kilometers each bus company's buses travel yearly?

d. kilometers each bus travels yearly?

e. riders each bus carries yearly?

f. kilometers each rider travels yearly?

62. In Canada, mining accounts for 17%, about $5,750,000,000, of the value of all goods produced. About how much is the total value of Canadian goods produced?

63. The formula $d = 4.8768t^2$ gives the number of meters an object will fall freely in t seconds, ignoring air resistance. Suppose a ball is dropped from the top of the Empire State Building. Ignoring air resistance,

a. how far will the ball fall in one second?

b. how far will the ball fall in two seconds?

c. how far will the ball fall in five seconds?

d. when the ball has fallen 238.9632 meters, how long has it fallen?

64. The Central State Telephone Co. sent Mr. Abbott a bill. It showed the following: base charge, \$9.14; extra calls within Central State, \$3.48; calls to other states, \$12.79. There is a 4% Central State tax on all Central State calls, including the base charge. There is a 6% federal tax on all telephone charges except taxes. What was the total bill?

65. In 1975, California's population was estimated at 22,077,000. This was an increase of about $40\frac{1}{2}$ % over California's 1960 population. About how much was California's 1960 population?

66. Mr. Miller bought a $1\frac{1}{2}$-kilogram can of coffee for $8.70. On the average, he uses 4 grams of coffee to make a cup of coffee. What is his average cost of a cup of coffee?

67. The total length of a golf course is figured by taking the distance from each tee to each hole and adding all the distances. Hairy Mountain Golf Course, an 18-hole course, is 6524 yards long. What is the average length of each hole? (Your answer should include yards, feet, and inches.)

68. Mr. Kriss teaches history. He always grades test papers on "the curve." That is, the highest 10% of the paper's get A's, and the lowest 10% get E's. The next 15% on each end get B's or D's. The rest get C's. All of the twenty students in one of Mr. Kriss's classes took the test he gave two days ago. How many got A's? B's? C's? D's? E's?

69. You go shopping. You see two sizes of the same product. You can use either size without waste. Tell which size is the better buy.

	first size		second size	
	size	**price**	**size**	**price**
a.	280 g	2 for 57¢	420 g	3 for 1.15
b.	680 g	75¢	900 g	98¢
c.	700 g	48¢	1200 g	85¢
d.	284 g	2 for 49¢	400 g	3 for 99¢

70. You want to buy a motorcycle for $800. The down payment is 30%. How much do you need for the down payment?

71. You drive from Big City to Smallville. You go the same speed all the way. It takes you $2\frac{1}{2}$ hours to get to the $\frac{1}{4}$ point. How long does it take you to get from Big City to the $\frac{3}{4}$ point?

72. Some years ago, the total value of goods produced in British Columbia was $2,906,962,000. Of this, 16% was forestry products, 14% was mineral products, 61% was manufactured products, 7% was agricultural products, and 2% was fish and fur products. What was the dollar value of the

a. forestry products?

b. mineral products?

c. manufactured products?

d. agricultural products?

e. fish and fur products?

73. Tomatoes sell at 2 cans for 55¢. How much will you be charged for 6 cans of tomatoes?

74. Twelve people can do a job in 4 days. How many people will it take (working at the same speed) to do the job in 3 days?

75. You buy some stock for $500. How much should you be able to sell it for now if the price is

a. 400% more?

b. 40% more?

c. .4% more?

76. A suit usually sells for $98.00. It is reduced in price by $\frac{1}{4}$.

a. How much is the discount?

b. What is the reduced price of the suit?

77. A store owner pays $225 for merchandise. To make a profit, he must sell it for at least 30% more than he pays. What is the least amount he must sell it for to show a profit?

78. It takes Mr. Jones 20% longer to do a job than it takes you to do it. You do the job in 30 minutes. How long does it take Mr. Jones to do the job?

79. At a supermarket, beets sell at 4 cans for 97¢. If you buy only one can of beets, how much will you be charged?

80. A student did 10 arithmetic problems. This was $\frac{2}{5}$ of the number assigned. How many problems were assigned?

81. You worked from 8:15 A.M. to 1:10 P.M. and from 1:35 P.M. to 5:25 P.M. How long did you work?

82. Ms. Kanten bought a set of tools for $750. She paid 25% down. There was a 16% yearly finance charge on the balance, which she agreed to pay in equal installments over a period of 18 months. How much was each monthly payment?

83. Imported ham sells for $1.19 a quarter-pound. How much will two pounds of it cost?

84. A bottle of shampoo costs $1.79 and lasts for 50 shampoos. A bottle of hair conditioner costs $2.78 and lasts for 75 treatments. Each time she shampoos her hair, Debby also uses the hair conditioner. Not counting the water used, what is the total cost of each of Debby's shampoos (to the nearest cent)?

85. Carpeting is on sale for $\frac{1}{3}$ off. A living room set is on sale for 20% off. Mr. and Mrs. Granler buy both. The usual price of the carpeting is $1,140. The usual price of the living room set is $900. How much do Mr. and Mrs. Granler pay?

86. Jerry wants to make a scale drawing of a side view of a car. The car is $5\frac{1}{2}$ meters long and $1\frac{1}{2}$ meters high. The paper Jerry has is 61 cm long and 30 cm wide. He wants to leave a margin of at least 3 cm all around the paper. What is the largest scale he can use?

87. At a supermarket, there is a 3% sales tax on everything sold except food. You go to this supermarket and buy items totaling $58.37 (not including sales tax). Of this amount, $29.58 is for food. The rest is not for food. How much is your total bill?

88. A wholesaler gives a store owner a 15% discount on the amount of a purchase. Besides this, a 20% discount is then given on the discounted price. The store owner's total purchase (before any discount) is $547.80. How much is he to pay the wholesaler?

89. Big City is 480 km from Ms. Jasper's home. On the way there, she drove at a steady speed of 80 kph. On the way back, she drove at a steady speed of 60 kph. What was her average speed for the round trip?

90. A ranch owner in Texas had 5,000 steers. He gave $\frac{1}{2}$ of them to his oldest son. He gave 30% of the rest to his brother. He sold $\frac{3}{14}$ of the number still left to another rancher. How many steers did he

a. give to his oldest son?

b. give to his brother?

c. sell to the other rancher?

d. end up with?

Chapter 9

Mixed Concepts 3

INSTRUCTIONS

A. No problem is meant to trick you.

Example

Problem: You buy meat for $3.87. You give the cashier $5. How much change do you get?

Answer: $1.13 (Assume you pay the full price for the meat. Assume you don't buy anything else. Assume there is no sales tax. Assume the cashier gives you the correct change.)

B. You are given all the information you need to solve each problem.

Example

Problem: Oranges sell for 90¢ a dozen. You buy 8 oranges. You give the cashier 75¢. How much change do you get?

Answer: 15¢ (Assume you can buy part of a dozen at the price of 90¢ a dozen. Assume you don't buy anything else. Assume the cashier charges you the right amount. Assume the cashier gives you the right amount of change.)

C. If the answer is a fraction, write it in reduced form.

Example

Problem: Forty people shared 10 pies. How much did each person get?

Answer: $\frac{1}{4}$ pie (We get an answer of $\frac{10}{40}$ pie, which we reduce to $\frac{1}{4}$ pie.)

D. Do not round off any answer unless the problem makes it right to do so.

Example

Problem: Peas sell at 3 cans for $1.01. You buy one can of peas. How much will you be charged?

Answer: $.34 or 34¢ (You can't pay a store a fractional part of one cent.)

E. Assume that a business will always round a part of a cent up, not down, when you are to pay.

Example

Problem: Peas sell at 3 cans for $1. You buy one can of peas. How much will you be charged?

Answer: $.34 or 34¢ (not $.33 or 33¢—Also, you can't pay a store a fractional part of one cent.)

F. If an answer is not about money, and if the problem does not tell you how many decimal places to use, then carry the division to two decimal places unless you have a zero remainder before then.

Example

Problem: Write $\frac{49}{16}$ as a decimal.

Answer: $3.06\frac{1}{4}$ (not $3\frac{1}{16}$, not $3.0\frac{5}{8}$, not $3.062\frac{1}{2}$, and not 3.0625)

G. In general, if a percent is not a whole number, write the remainder as a fraction, not as a decimal.

Example

Problem: Rawlins earned $20,000 last year. This year she will earn $24,000. What percent of this year's earnings were last year's earnings?

Answer: $83\frac{1}{3}$% (not 83.3% or 83.33% or 83.333%, etc.)

1. One third of Mr. Harper's class are boys. 60% of Mr. Green's class are boys. There are 27 students in Mr. Harper's class. There are 25 students in Mr. Green's class. There are 6 boys who are in both Mr. Harper's and Mr. Green's classes. How many boys are in only one of the two classes?

2. A jetliner takes 4 hours and 15 minutes to fly from Detroit to Los Angeles. The air distance is 1,976 miles. What is the average speed of the plane (to the nearest tenth of a mile an hour)?

3. A pound of grass seed will seed 300 square feet of ground, if all the seeds germinate. Ms. Markey wants to seed her front and back yards. The front yard will be 50 feet by 30 feet. The back yard will be 40 feet by 60 feet. The seed she wants has a 90% germination rate. How many pounds should she buy? (Assume that she cannot buy a part of a pound.)

4. When driving his car, Mr. Tyler's reaction time between seeing a danger and hitting the brake pedal is $\frac{1}{2}$ second. If he drives 72 kph, how many meters does his car go in that $\frac{1}{2}$ second?

5. As shown below, a parking lot charges for time a car is parked there. The full amount is charged for any time in that price range. For example, if the charge is $1.00 an hour and you were parked there only $\frac{1}{2}$ hour, you still have to pay $1.00.

$1.50 for the first half-hour
$2.00 for the next hour
$1.00 for each of the next 3 hours
$ .50 for each of the next 19 hours
$ .50 for the next half-hour

The schedule starts over at the end of each 24-hour period. Tell how much the charge will be if you park your car in the lot for the times shown in each problem.

a. You park from 8:00 A.M. until 11:45 A.M.

b. You park from 9:15 A.M. until 4:48 P.M.

c. You park from 9:15 A.M. one day until 11:45 A.M. the next day.

d. You park from 8:37 A.M. until 2:15 P.M.

e. You park from 8:30 A.M. until 2:30 A.M.

6. Mr. Ino's class took a test. Half of the students scored at least 80%. Two-thirds of the others scored at least 70%. There were 30 students in the class. How many scored below 70%?

7. To figure out the selling price of groceries, a supermarket adds an average of 15% to its cost of the groceries. The market's sales of groceries one day totaled $5,060. How much was its profit on the groceries that day?

8. A racehorse averages 35 miles an hour when running around a one-mile track. How long (in minutes and/or seconds) does it take the horse to run the mile?

9. The circumference of a circular island is 7854 kilometers. Its area is 4,908.750 square kilometers. How long is its radius?

10. A car travels 600 kilometers at an average speed of 60 kph. On the return trip, the car averages 50 kph. What was its average speed for the entire 1200 kilometers?

11. A grocery owner buys a crate of apples for $9.72. The apples weigh 30 kilograms. The owner figures that 10% of the apples will spoil before they can be sold. The selling price of the apples which are to be sold must total $33\frac{1}{3}$ % more than the cost of the crate of apples. For how much a kilogram are the apples to be sold?

12. Juliet wants to make a muumuu. She can buy material either in a 1-meter width or in a $1\frac{1}{2}$-meter width. She figures she will need $4\frac{1}{2}$ meters of the 1-meter material, or she will need 3 meters of the $1\frac{1}{2}$-meter material. The 1-meter material sells for $4.50 a meter. The $1\frac{1}{2}$-meter material sells for $6.50 a meter.

    a. Which material will cost Juliet less?

    b. How much will she save if she buys this less expensive material?

13. A swimming pool is filled to an average depth of 8 feet. The pool is 30 feet wide and 50 feet long. There are 231 cubic inches of water in a gallon of water. How many gallons (to the nearest whole gallon) of water does it take to fill the pool?

14. The odometer and the speedometer of a car are both set in the factory. The factory sets them according to the size of the rear-wheel tire the car is supposed to use.

    a. Your tire treads are worn down. The speedometer shows the car is going 60 kph. Is the car really going faster than, or slower than, 60 kph?

    b. Your tire treads are worn down. The odometer shows the car traveled 10 kilometers. Did the car really travel more than, or less than, 10 kilometers?

    c. You put larger (bigger diameter) tires on the rear wheels than the car manual says to use. Will the speedometer show a speed more than, or less than, the speed the car is really going? Explain.

15. The Cardenas Dam in Mexico is 787 feet long and 302 feet high. The volume of material in the dam is about 7,000,000 cubic yards. Suppose that the dam's vertical wall is the same width from bottom to top. Then how many feet wide is the dam (to the nearest whole foot)?

16. Ms. Andrews stays in a hotel room for 3 days. There is a 9% state tax on room rentals. The room charge is $35 a day, not including the tax. She also charges $8.45 in telephone calls and $25.67 in meals to her room. How much is her total hotel bill?

17. Mr. Zender stays in a hotel room for 4 days. There is a 9% state tax on room rentals. His total bill is $192.24, including the room, the tax, and each of the following: $9.34 a day for meals; $2.75 a day for phone calls.

a. How much is the charge for his room, including the tax?

b. How much is the tax?

18. The local ice cream store gives you a choice of ice cream cones. You can get a cone with two scoops of ice cream for 50¢, or you can get a cone with three scoops of ice cream for 60¢. The diameter of a scoop for the two-scoop cone is $2\frac{3}{4}$ inches. The diameter of a scoop for the three-scoop cone is $2\frac{1}{2}$ inches. Which cone gives you more ice cream for your money? (The formula for the volume of a sphere is $V = \frac{4}{3}\pi r^3$.)

19. A lever balances on a fulcrum. When you push down on one end, the other end goes up. The part of the lever between you and the fulcrum is called the effort arm. The part between the fulcrum and the other end is called the load arm. The length of the effort arm times the amount of effort on it equals the length of the load arm times the amount of effort on it. (Example: Suppose the effort arm is 3 feet long and the load arm is 2 feet long. If you put 10 pounds of weight on the effort arm, it will lift 15 pounds of weight. This is, 3 feet × 10 pounds = 2 feet × 15 pounds.)

a. The effort arm of a 5-foot lever is 3 feet long. You apply 50 pounds to the effort arm. How many pounds will the load arm lift?

b. The effort arm of a 5-foot lever is 4 feet long. You apply 50 pounds to the effort arm. How many pounds will the load arm lift?

c. You have a 4-foot crowbar and want to move a 300-pound rock. You are able to use 100 pounds of effort. Where should you place the fulcrum?

d. Zora and Jeff want to play on a seesaw. The seesaw is 10 feet long. Zora weighs 75 pounds. Jeff weighs 50 pounds. How far from Zora should the fulcrum be?

20. The lengths of the shadows cast by two objects in the sun is directly proportional to the heights of the objects. That is, $\frac{\text{length of shadow of \#1}}{\text{length of shadow of \#2}} = \frac{\text{height of \#1}}{\text{height of \#2}}$.

a. Royce is $5\frac{1}{2}$ feet tall. His shadow is 4 feet long. The shadow of the tree in his front yard is 20 feet long. How high is the top of the tree?

b. Jane is 155 cm tall. A 620-cm flagpole's shadow is 500 cm long. How long is Jane's shadow?

21. In astronomy, a light year is the distance light travels in a year. The speed of light is 299,792 kilometers a second.

a. How far is a light year? (Use $365\frac{1}{4}$ days for year.)

b. Earth is an average distance of 149,590,000 kilometers from the sun. How long (in minutes and seconds) does it take light to reach Earth from the sun?

22. In a bowling league, the largest ball permitted has a circumference of 60 cm. To the nearest tenth, what is the volume of this ball? (Use $\pi = 3.1416$.)

23. Ms. Sanders ate at a restaurant. She spent a total of $9.00, including a tip of 20% on the cost of the meal.

a. How much was the meal?

b. How much was the tip?

24. In a bowling league, a "spot" between two teams is figured as follows: For each team, the league averages of its members are totaled. The spot is 70% (to the nearest whole number) of the difference. Team A will bowl against Team B tomorrow. The league averages of Team A's members are 170, 169, 194, 175, and 167. The league averages of Team B's members are 165, 160, 191, 187, and 154. How much is the spot?

25. In business, "gross profit" and "markup" are the same in dollars, but they are different in percents. In dollars, they are the difference between selling price and cost of goods. This difference is then used to figure the two percents needed. It is done as follows: (1) The percent of gross profit is the difference between selling price and cost of goods times 100% divided by the selling price. (2) The percent of markup is the same difference times 100% divided by the cost.

Example: A grocery store pays $100 for food and sells it for $125. Both the gross profit and the markup are $25. The percent of gross profit is $\frac{\$25 \times 100\%}{\$125} = 20\%$ and the percent of markup is $\frac{\$25 \times 100\%}{\$100} = 25\%$.

Figure out a way to fill in the missing percents below.

	% of gross profit	% of markup
a.	10	
b.	15	
c.	20	
d.	25	
e.	30	
f.	$33\frac{1}{3}$	
g.	40	
h.	50	
i.	$66\frac{2}{3}$	
j.	75	

26. Use the figures from problem 25.

a. A businessperson pays $100 for goods. A gross profit of $33\frac{1}{3}$ % is needed. How much should the selling price be?

b. A grocery owner pays $3.65 for a 24-can case of spinach. A gross profit of 20% is needed. What should be the selling price for a can of spinach?

c. A novelty store pays $35.50 for 100 novelty items. All are to be sold at the same price. A 75% gross profit is needed. What should be the selling price of each item?

27. The amount of light reaching a place varies in inverse proportion to the square of the distance from the light source. (That is, the light is brighter when you are close to it, and it is dimmer when you are far from it.) Ann is 60 cm away from a light source. Ken is 90 cm away from the same light source. How many times brighter is it where Ann is than where Ken is?

28. Mr. Sherber is going to plant flower seeds along a 35-meter lawn border. Each package of seeds will cover about $1\frac{1}{2}$ meters of the border if all the seeds germinate. How many packages of seeds should he buy if the seeds have an 85% germination rate?

29. A telephone company has three kinds of dial-direct rates: weekday (full rate); evening (35% discount from the full rate); night and weekend (60% discount from the full rate). The weekday rate is used Monday through Friday, 8:00 A.M. to 5:00 P.M. The evening rate is used Sunday through Friday, 5:00 P.M. to 11:00 P.M. The night and weekend rate is used all other times. The charge is based on the time the call is answered, not the time the call is ended. (For example, a Monday call answered at 4:55 P.M. and ended at 5:15 P.M. is charged at the weekday rate.) The following weekday rates are in effect for calls from Big City:

To	First Minute	Each Additional Minute
Atlanta	50¢	34¢
Chicago	46¢	32¢
Denver	52¢	36¢
Seattle	54¢	38¢

Any part of a minute is charged as a full minute. Find the charge on each of the following calls from Big City:

a. On Sunday Mr. Wilson dials a number in Seattle at 9:00 A.M. The call is answered immediately. The call is over at 9:17 A.M. How much is the charge?

b. Mr. Wilson calls the same number at 6:00 P.M. the same day. The connection lasts for 17 minutes. How much is the charge?

c. The next day, Mr. Wilson calls the same number again. This time the call is made at 10:00 A.M. Again, the call lasts for 17 minutes. How much is the charge?

d. On Wednesday, Ms. Young's dialed call to Chicago is answered at 9:00 A.M. The call is finished at 9:25 A.M. How much is the charge?

e. On Friday, Ms. Joplin's dialed call to Denver is answered at 5:07 P.M. Both parties hang up at 5:58 P.M. How much is the charge?

f. On Monday, Mr. Horner dials Atlanta at 11:10 P.M., and his party answers right away. They hang up at 11:33 P.M. How much is the charge?

30. Everyday Finance Co. loans money. Monthly interest on the unpaid balance is charged as follows: $2\frac{1}{2}$ % on the first $100; 2% on the next $150; $1\frac{1}{2}$ % on the next $150; $1\frac{1}{4}$ % on any balance over $400. Mr. and Mrs. Marner borrow $500 from Everyday Finance Co. Their monthly payments are $90, including interest. Complete the schedule below.

Date of Payment	Total Payment	Interest	Principal	Balance Due
3/15	Amount Borrowed			$500.00
4/15	$90.00			
5/15	$90.00			
6/15	$90.00			
7/15	$90.00			
8/15	$90.00			

31. Mr. and Mrs. Kramer also borrow $500 from Everyday Finance Co. Their monthly payments are also $90, including interest. A "month" has the number of days there are from one payment date to the same day the next month. (In the problem on the previous page, the "month" from the 4/15 to the 5/15 payment has 30 days. The "month" from the 5/15 payment to the 6/15 payment has 31 days.) If a payment is made early or late, then the interest charge is adjusted accordingly. For example, if the 6/15 payment is made on 6/20, then interest is charged for an extra 5 days. That is, the interest charge is $\frac{36}{31}$ of the normal interest charge. Fill in the schedule below.

Date of Payment	Total Payment	Interest	Principal	Balance Due
3/15	Amount Borrowed			$500.00
4/10	$90.00			
5/20	$90.00			
6/25	$90.00			
7/15	$90.00			
8/25	$90.00			

32. A covered truck bed is 7 feet wide, 12 feet long, and 6 feet high. It is to be loaded with packing crates which are $1\frac{1}{2}$ feet wide, 3 feet long, and $1\frac{3}{4}$ feet high.

a. What is the capacity (volume) of the truck bed?

b. What is the volume of each packing crate?

c. How many whole packing crates can be fitted in the truck bed?

d. What volume of the truck bed will be unused after the packing crates are fitted in?

33. Mr. Eaton drove his car on a 600-kilometer trip. He drove 80 kilometers an hour for $\frac{2}{3}$ of the way, and he drove 60 kilometers an hour the rest of the way.

a. How long did the trip take him?

b. What was his average speed?

34. A covered truck bed is 7 feet wide, 12 feet long, and 6 feet high. It is to be loaded with packing crates which are $1\frac{3}{4}$ feet wide, 3 feet long, and $1\frac{3}{4}$ feet high.
   a. What is the capacity (volume) of the truck bed?

   b. What is the volume of each packing crate?

   c. How many whole packing crates can be fitted in the truck bed?

   d. What volume of the truck bed will be unused after the packing crates are fitted in?

35. A jetliner left the St. Louis air terminal at 7:00 P.M. and arrived at a Detroit air terminal at 9:05 P.M. The distance between the air terminals is 462 miles.
   a. To the nearest tenth, what was the average speed of the jetliner?

   b. To the nearest whole number, what was the average speed of the jetliner?

36. A salesperson was to attend a convention in a distant city. Her boss asked how much it would probably cost. The salesperson figured the following: air fare, $250; hotel bill, 4 days at $35, plus 8% room tax; meals, 13 at $4.50; mileage to and from the airport, 70 miles at 20¢ a mile; airport parking fee, $9.75; telephone calls, $15; miscellaneous, $10. Suppose these figures were correct. How much did it cost the company to have the salesperson attend the convention (not counting the salesperson's salary or the sales lost because the salesperson was at the convention)?

37. A supermarket makes a gross profit of 5% on coffee and on soap. It makes a 20% gross profit on canned vegetables and soup. It makes a 30% gross profit on fresh fruits and vegetables. The market's sales one day were as follows: canned vegetables, \$300; coffee, \$200; fresh vegetables, \$100; canned soup, \$150; soap, \$350; fresh fruit, \$150. How much was the market's total gross profit on these items that day?

38. You want to tile a room which is 20 feet by 30 feet. The tiles are each 9 inches square. You may have to cut some tiles. But you do not want to put two or more part-tiles together to make either a whole tile or another part-tile.

a. What is the area of the room to be tiled?

b. How many tiles will it take to do the job the way you want to do it?

c. The tiles are on sale for \$1.75 a dozen. How many dozen will you need to buy?

d. How much will the tile cost?

39. A room is 14 feet 5 inches by 15 feet 7 inches. What is its area (in square feet)?

40. You are payroll clerk in a company. Workers are paid three rates: straight time (the hourly rate); time and a half ($1\frac{1}{2}$ times the hourly rate); double time (twice the hourly rate).

A worker gets straight time except as follows. The worker gets time and a half for any time worked over 8 hours in one day or for any work on a Saturday. The worker gets double time for any time worked on a Sunday or a holiday or for any time worked over 8 hours on a Saturday. (If a holiday falls on, say, Tuesday, then the worker gets double time for all time worked that Tuesday.)

In each problem which follows, you are given the worker's hourly rate and the number of hours worked each day in the week. An asterisk (*) following a number of hours means that that day was a holiday. Figure out each worker's gross pay (that is, the pay before any payroll deductions for taxes, etc.). Show all of your work.

	Hourly Rate	Sun.	Mon.	Tues.	Wed.	Thurs.	Fri.	Sat.	Gross Pay
a.	$4.50	0	8	8	8	8	8	0	
b.	$4.50	0	10	8	8	8	8	0	
c.	$4.50	0	0	8	8	8	8	8	
d.	$4.50	8	8	8	8	8	8	8	
e.	$4.50	8	10	12	8	6	10	10	
f.	$4.50	8	8*	10	10	8	10	8	
g.	$5.82	8	8	10	8	8	8	10	
h.	$6.75	0	0	0	10	12*	10	10	
i.	$7.85	2	8	8	7	9	10	6	

41. You are still a payroll clerk for the same company. The company installs a time clock for its hourly workers. Overtime rates are the same as before. Time is computed to $\frac{1}{10}$ of an hour. When punching in, a worker is allowed a two-minute leeway for each $\frac{1}{10}$-hour period. After that two minutes, the worker is counted as arriving in the next $\frac{1}{10}$-hour period. (If Mr. Smith punches in at 8:02 A.M., he is paid starting at 8:00 A.M. If he punches in from 8:03 A.M. to 8:08 A.M., he is paid starting at 8:06 A.M.) When punching out, the worker is paid to the last previous $\frac{1}{10}$ -hour period unless the time falls on a $\frac{1}{10}$-hour period. (If Ms. Jones punches out at any time from 4:00 P.M. to 4:05 P.M., she is paid until 4:00 P.M. If she punches out at any time from 4:06 P.M. until 4:11 P.M., she is paid until 4:06 P.M.)

In the chart which follows, read down for each problem. You are given the hourly rate, the time punched in, and the time punched out for each day. Figure out each worker's gross pay for the week. Show all of your work.

Problem	a.	b.	c.	d.	e.
Hourly Rate	$5.76	$8.19	$7.75	$4.50	$5.10
Sun.		I 7:00 O 2:00	I 6:30 O 11:30 I 12:18 O 4:00	I 6:30 O 11:30 I 12:12 O 4:00	I 6:30 O 11:30 I 12:30 O 4:02
Mon.	I 8:24 O 12:00 I 12:30 O 4:30	I 8:00 O 12:00 I 1:00 O 5:00	I 6:30 O 11:30 I 12:18 O 4:00	I 6:30 O 11:30 I 12:12 O 4:00	I 6:32 O 11:36 I 12:30 O 4:06
Tues.	I 10:12 O 2:00	I 9:00 O 1:00		I 7:45 O 11:30 I 1:00 O 5:05	
Wed.			I 7:35 O 11:35		
Thurs.	I 6:30 O 10:30				I 6:40 O 10:40
Fri.			I 6:30 O 10:30		
Sat.	I 6:30 O 11:30	I 7:00 O 11:05	I 8:03 O 11:30		

42. A nationwide trucking company picks up and delivers packages anywhere in the continental United States except Alaska. The fee for this service depends on the weight of the package and the distance it is to be delivered.

- First, there is a service charge of $2.00.
- Next, there is a weight charge as follows:

  $2.00 for the first kilogram

  $1.00/kilogram for each of the next 5 kilograms

  $ .50/kilogram for each kilogram over 6 kilograms

  The weight charge is not adjusted for fractional kilograms. For example, the weight charge for a 3-kilogram package would be the same as for a $2\frac{1}{2}$-kilogram package—that is, $4.00.

- The base charge is the total of the service charge and the weight charge.
- Finally, the distance charge is as follows:

Distance in km		Add this percent of base charge
at least	but less than	
0	15	0
15	80	20
80	160	30
160	400	40
400	800	50
800	1600	65
1600	2400	80
2400	3200	95
over 3200		110

Example Problem:

A 5-kilogram package is to be delivered a distance of 95 kilometers. What is the trucking company's charge?

Solution:

$2.00 service charge
$6.00 weight charge ($2.00 + 4 × $1.00)
$8.00 base charge
$2.40 distance charge (add 30% of base charge)
$10.40 total charge

For each problem below, compute the trucking company's charge. Show your work.

a. A 5-kg package is to be delivered a distance of 500 km.

b. A 9-kg package is to be delivered a distance of 10 km.

c. A 7-kg package is to be delivered a distance of 1600 km.

d. A $6\frac{1}{2}$-kg package is to be delivered a distance of 25 km.

e. A 12.4-kg package is to be delivered a distance of 2400 km.

f. A 3.4-kg package is to be delivered a distance of 98 km.

43. These problems will give you practice in figuring out a bowling score. For each problem, use a bowling score sheet like the ones shown, and show the running score.

SCORING

Bowling is scored in "frames." There are 10 frames per game, and each bowler receives two tries per frame to knock down as many of the 10 pins as possible. There are three scoring possibilities per frame: (1) the bowler knocks down fewer than 10 pins with two balls, (2) the bowler knocks down all 10 pins with two balls (a spare), (3) the bowler knocks down all 10 pins with the first ball (a strike).

A strike counts as 10 pins plus the total number of pins that the bowler knocks down with the next two balls. A spare counts as 10 pins plus the number of pins the bowler knocks down with the next ball.

If the bowler scores a strike or a spare in the tenth frame, he or she rolls extra balls. If the bowler scores a strike on the first ball in the 10th frame, he or she receives two extra throws. If the bowler scores a spare in the 10th frame, he or she receives one extra throw. A bowler never bowls more than three balls in the 10th frame.

USING THE SCORE SHEET

Frames are represented on the score sheet by ten numbered, divided boxes (see below). Each frame on the score sheet (except the tenth) has two small boxes for recording the numbers of pins knocked down in that frame and a larger open area for keeping track of the running score. There are three small squares in the last frame to accommodate the extra throws awarded to bowlers bowling a strike or a spare in the 10th frame.

The pins knocked down are indicated in the two small squares at the top right corner of each frame. The three possible scores are shown on the score sheet as follows: (1) When fewer than 10 pins are knocked down, the number of pins knocked down with the first ball is written in the first (leftmost) small square, and the number of pins knocked down with the second ball is written in the second small square. If no pins are knocked down with a particular ball, a dash is entered in the small square. (2) When a spare is thrown, the number of pins knocked down with the first ball goes in the first small square, as usual, and a diagonal line is used in the second small square. (3) A strike is shown by marking an X in the first of the two small squares. The second small square remains blank.

The running total for the score is written in the larger space of each frame. After frame 1, the total for each new frame is added to the totals of the previous frames to get a running total. Note that you can't add the total for strikes or spares into the running total until all the balls that count for the strike's or spare's score have been played. In an actual game, the figure for the running total may be one or two frames behind the frame of play.

1	2	3	4	5	6	7	8	9	10	Total

a. The table below shows the results of a game of bowling. Fill in the score sheet, and find the total score.

Frame	First Ball	Second Ball
1	5	4
2	7	3
3	10	
4	8	2
5	10	
6	10	
7	10	
8	7	3
9	6	3
10	4	3

1	2	3	4	5	6	7	8	9	10	Total

b. The table below shows the results of a game of bowling. Fill in the score sheet, and find the total score.

Frame	First Ball	Second Ball	
1	10		
2	10		
3	7	2	
4	6	3	
5	9	1	
6	9	1	
7	8	2	
8	10		
9	10		
10	8	2	Third ball = 9

1	2	3	4	5	6	7	8	9	10	Total

c. What is the maximum possible score a bowler can receive? Show on the score sheet how this score would be recorded.

1	2	3	4	5	6	7	8	9	10	Total

Chapter 10

Answers

Chapter 1: Introductory

1. $30
2. $50
3. $400
4. $4
5. 3
6. 4
7. 4
8. 3
9. 30
10. 50 mpg
11. **a.** $\frac{1}{4}$ **b.** 4
12. 400 kilometers
13. $30
14. 3
15. $400
16. $50
17. 3
18. $4
19. $400
20. $30
21. $50
22. $400
23. 50 minutes
24. 30 minutes
25. 400 minutes
26. $400
27. 3
28. $30
29. $50
30. $4
31. 30 inches
32. 400
33. 4
34. 4
35. 4
36. $50
37. $30
38. 3 hours
39. 30
40. $400
41. 50 pounds
42. 4
43. 3
44. $\frac{1}{4}$ pound
45. 4
46. 3
47. 50
48. 30 ounces
49. 400
50. 3
51. $50
52. $30
53. $4
54. 3
55. $400
56. $30
57. 3
58. 400
59. 30
60. 50
61. 4
62. 400¢ or $4
63. 3
64. $50
65. 4
66. $30
67. 3
68. $30
69. $400
70. $30
71. $50
72. $400
73. $4
74. 3
75. $50
76. 4
77. 50
78. **a.** 30 **b.** 30
79. 400
80. 30 mph
81. 50
82. 400
83. 50 km
84. 3
85. 50
86. $50
87. 4
88. $400
89. 3
90. $30
91. $400
92. $4
93. **a.** 30 years **b.** 30 years **c.** 30
94. 400 years
95. 3
96. 4
97. 50 years
98. $\frac{1}{4}$
99. 4
100. 3
101. 30 pounds
102. 400 pounds
103. 4 pounds
104. 50 pounds
105. $50
106. $30 a share
107. $400
108. 4
109. 3
110. $400
111. 50 minutes
112. 30
113. 400 minutes
114. 3
115. 50
116. 4
117. **a.** $\frac{1}{4}$ **b.** $\frac{3}{4}$
118. 30

CHAPTER 1 CONT.

119. 400
120. 4
121. 30
122. 50
123. 4 meters
124. **a.** $\frac{1}{4}$ **b.** $\frac{3}{4}$ **c.** 3
125. 30 meters
126. 400 meters
127. $400
128. $30
129. $50
130. $4
131. $400
132. 3
133. 3
134. 30
135. 4
136. 50
137. 4
138. 400
139. 3
140. $30 a case
141. 3
142. $50
143. $400
144. 4
145. **a.** 30 **b.** 3 **c.** $\frac{1}{4}$ **d.** $\frac{3}{4}$
146. 4
147. 30
148. 50
149. 400
150. 4
151. 3
152. $50
153. $30
154. $400
155. **a.** $30 **b.** $\frac{1}{4}$ **c.** $\frac{3}{4}$
156. $50
157. $30
158. 4
159. 3
160. 30 liters
161. 4

CHAPTER 2: WHOLE NUMBERS

1. **a.** 30¢ **b.** 20¢
2. **a.** $100 **b.** $175
3. **a.** 20 **b.** 35
4. **a.** 60 **b.** 60 **c.** 24
5. 365
6. 18¢
7. **a.** 40 **b.** 2
8. 36¢
9. **a.** 100 **b.** 100 **c.** 100
10. 50 mph
11. **a.** 60¢ **b.** 140¢ **c.** 80¢
12. **a.** $18 **b.** $12 **c.** $3 **d.** $7 **e.** $5 **f.** $14 **g.** $27 **h.** $24
13. 60
14. 24
15. $18
16. **a.** 7 **b.** 52 **c.** 12
17. **a.** 7¢ **b.** 7¢
18. 45¢
19. 204 miles
20. 80 km
21. 13
22. **a.** 98¢ **b.** 2¢
23. **a.** 36 months **b.** 5 years **c.** 50 months **d.** 6 years 5 months
24. 88 sq. in.
25. 819 kph
26. $15,000 a year
27. **a.** 7 **b.** 12 **c.** 3
28. $242
29. $2,964
30. 368
31. 720¢
32. **a.** 264¢ **b.** 236¢
33. 385
34. 665¢
35. 180 square feet
36. **a.** 3 hours 55 minutes **b.** 4 hours 15 minutes **c.** 5 hours 10 minutes
37. 86,400
38. $125
39. **a.** 300¢ **b.** $5
40. **a.** 12 **b.** 3 **c.** 5,280
41. 8 hours
42. $200 a week
43. $170
44. 18¢
45. 60
46. **a.** 60 inches **b.** 108 inches **c.** 4 feet **d.** 8 yards
47. 1 inch
48. **a.** 2 teaspoons **b.** 3 teaspoons
49. 168
50. **a.** 29 **b.** 16 **c.** 33
51. **a.** 110¢ **b.** 275¢
52. 112¢
53. $2,138
54. 475 mph
55. **a.** 1,000 **b.** 1,000 **c.** 1,000
56. **a.** 144 miles **b.** 320 miles **c.** 11 **d.** 15
57. **a.** 105 **b.** 85
58. $40
59. **a.** 342¢ **b.** 158¢
60. **a.** 344 **b.** 86
61. **a.** 3 weeks **b.** 49 days
62. **a.** 27 **b.** 18
63. 63,360
64. **a.** 16 **b.** 2 **c.** 4
65. 445
66. **a.** 26¢ **b.** 13¢ **c.** 2080¢ **d.** 18 **e.** 27 dozen (or 324) **f.** 30
67. $7,500
68. 30
69. **a.** 6 **b.** 1 **c.** 4 **d.** 8 **e.** 36 **f.** 20
70. **a.** 4 feet 10 inches **b.** 6 feet 4 inches **c.** 9 feet 6 inches
71. **a.** $17 **b.** $9

CHAPTER 2 CONT.

72. 3,600
73. **a.** \$89 **b.** \$75 **c.** \$16 **d.** \$47 **e.** \$21 **f.** \$13 **g.** \$165 **h.** \$201
74. 17
75. 320 miles
76. **a.** 16 to 5 **b.** 5 to 16 **c.** 36 to 32 or 9 to 8 **d.** 32 to 36 or 8 to 9
77. 77
78. 80
79. **a.** 144 **b.** 9 **c.** 10,000
80. **a.** 54 **b.** 114
81. 792
82. **a.** \$280 **b.** \$320 **c.** \$360 **d.** \$312 **e.** \$328
83. **a.** \$7 **b.** \$42
84. 26
85. 80 kph
86. **a.** \$64 **b.** \$280 **c.** 15 hours **d.** 39 hours
87. **a.** 2 **b.** \$9 **c.** \$18 **d.** \$108
88. **a.** 150¢ **b.** 350¢ **c.** 6 **d.** 30
89. 44
90. **a.** 13 mpg **b.** 17 mpg
91. **a.** \$27,000 **b.** \$26,400 **c.** He made \$600 more two years ago.
92. 45
93. **a.** 24 **b.** 6 **c.** 6 **d.** 3
94. **a.** \$31 **b.** \$55 **c.** 5 **d.** 8
95. **a.** 2 dozen **b.** 3 **c.** 27 **d.** 8 **e.** 3 **f.** 7
96. 16 inches
97. **a.** 10:10 **b.** 10:10 **c.** 2:15
98. 60
99. **a.** 3 pounds 15 ounces **b.** 8 pounds 7 ounces **c.** 7 pounds 1 ounce **d.** 9 pounds 11 ounces
100. **a.** 360 km **b.** 5 **c.** 72 kph (Point out that the average is not just $\frac{60+80}{2}$ kph = 70 kph.)
101. 15¢
102. 12
103. \$100
104. **a.** 234 square feet **b.** 26 square yards **c.** \$338
105. **a.** 410 **b.** 1,640 **c.** 1,071 **d.** 1,428 **e.** 1,176 **f.** 392
106. \$65
107. 9
108. **a.** 5 meters **b.** 200 cm **c.** 4,000 meters **d.** 300,000 cm
109. **a.** \$4 **b.** \$7 **c.** 4 hours **d.** 9 hours
110. \$7,400
111. 48 kph
112. **a.** \$60 **b.** 50 **c.** 150 **d.** \$40
113. **a.** 80 **b.** 75
114. **a.** 9 **b.** 3 **c.** 12
115. **a.** 32 ounces **b.** 5 pounds
116. 12 square feet
117. 95
118. \$31
119. 16 inches long and 10 inches high
120. 10¢
121. **a.** 3 meters 90 centimeters **b.** 8 meters 40 centimeters **c.** 5 meters 15 centimeters
122. **a.** 10¢ **b.** 18¢ **c.** 66¢ **d.** 5 minutes **e.** 10 minutes **f.** 3 minutes
123. 63 kph

CHAPTER 3: FRACTIONS

1. $1\frac{4}{5}$
2. $\frac{5}{9}$
3. $1\frac{5}{12}$
4. **a.** $\frac{5}{6}$ year **b.** $\frac{35}{52}$ year **c.** $\frac{5}{7}$ week
5. **a.** \$160 **b.** \$240
6. **a.** $5\frac{11}{12}$ **b.** \$$53\frac{1}{4}$ or \$53.25
7. **a.** $61\frac{1}{4}$ **b.** \$490 **c.** $30\frac{5}{8}$ **d.** $18\frac{3}{4}$
8. 50
9. \$240
10. **a.** 10 ml water, 4 ml acid **b.** 50 ml
11. 202¢ or \$2.02
12. 150¢ or \$1.50
13. $29\frac{1}{6}$ ¢
14. $2\frac{2}{3}$ cups
15. **a.** $15\frac{5}{12}$ **b.** $5\frac{5}{36}$ **c.** \$$92\frac{1}{2}$ or \$92.50
16. **a.** $\frac{7}{12}$ hour **b.** $1\frac{1}{2}$ hours **c.** $3\frac{1}{3}$ hours
17. $29\frac{2}{5}$
18. 32¢
19. 4 inches by $5\frac{1}{6}$ inches
20. $1\frac{1}{4}$ meter
21. $\frac{11}{16}$
22. **a.** $2\frac{3}{7}$ weeks **b.** $1\frac{43}{52}$ years **c.** $2\frac{15}{52}$ years
23. **a.** $2\frac{9}{20}$ **b.** 3
24. **a.** 98¢ **b.** 120¢ or \$1.20
25. **a.** \$30 **b.** \$90 **c.** \$15
26. 60 kph
27. **a.** $1\frac{1}{2}$ pounds **b.** $3\frac{1}{2}$ pounds
28. $10\frac{2}{5}$
29. **a.** $\frac{1}{2}$ **b.** 45¢
30. 50 kph
31. $4\frac{1}{3}$
32. **a.** $1\frac{5}{6}$ **b.** \$$16\frac{1}{2}$ or \$16.50

CHAPTER 3 CONT.

33. **a.** 56 **b.** 14
34. **a.** $20\frac{3}{4}$ **b.** $4\frac{3}{20}$ **c.** \$$207\frac{1}{2}$ or \$207.50 **d.** \$$41\frac{1}{2}$ or \$41.50
35. $\frac{1}{8}$ inch
36. $\frac{7}{8}$ inch
37. $\frac{7}{8}$ inch
38. 88 kph
39. $7\frac{2}{3}$
40. **a.** $\frac{7}{12}$ foot **b.** $1\frac{2}{3}$ feet **c.** 52 inches
41. **a.** add to **b.** $\frac{1}{6}$ cup
42. **a.** $4\frac{1}{12}$ **b.** $2\frac{1}{24}$ **c.** 147¢ or \$1.47 **d.** $\frac{11}{12}$
43. Gwen is $5\frac{5}{12}$ years older than Edith.
44. **a.** $4\frac{1}{3}$ weeks **b.** 13 weeks **c.** $1\frac{11}{13}$ months
45. $2\frac{1}{3}$
46. \$90
47. $439\frac{1}{9}$ mph
48. $431\frac{7}{55}$ mph
49. **a.** $23\frac{1}{2}$ inches long, $11\frac{1}{2}$ inches high, $17\frac{1}{2}$ inches deep **b.** $1\frac{23}{24}$ feet long, $\frac{23}{24}$ foot high, $1\frac{11}{24}$ feet deep
50. \$$12\frac{1}{2}$ or \$12.50
51. **a.** $\frac{1}{3}$ **b.** $\frac{3}{5}$ **c.** $3\frac{1}{15}$
52. $4\frac{1}{12}$
53. **a.** \$180 **b.** \$450 **c.** \$50 **d.** \$40
54. \$96
55. 1 cm = $36\frac{1}{2}$ km
56. **a.** $\frac{29}{50}$ meter **b.** 325 cm **c.** $\frac{13}{4000}$ km
57. $\frac{7}{10}$ mph
58. $12\frac{5}{6}$ cm
59. **a.** \$$4\frac{4}{9}$ or about \$4.44 **b.** \$$7\frac{5}{16}$ or about \$7.31 **c.** \$6
60. **a.** $14\frac{1}{4}$ **b.** $7\frac{1}{8}$
61. **a.** $4\frac{1}{3}$ **b.** $3\frac{5}{6}$ **c.** $8\frac{1}{6}$
62. 15 inches by 21 inches
63. $\frac{7}{15}$
64. \$1,040
65. 2286¢ or \$22.86
66. **a.** \$7,500 **b.** \$625 **c.** \$$144\frac{3}{13}$ or about \$144.23
67. 171
68. $1\frac{13}{16}$ inches by $1\frac{13}{16}$ inches
69. 12
70. \$180
71. \$10
72. 340 km
73. 276 km
74. $\frac{1}{4}$
75. $6\frac{2}{3}$
76. \$495
77. **a.** $\frac{3}{4}$ **b.** \$37,500
78. **a.** $\frac{3}{20}$ **b.** $\frac{1}{20}$ **c.** food, \$$60\frac{3}{10}$ or \$60.30; household supplies, \$$20\frac{1}{10}$ or \$20.10
79. \$9,500
80. $\frac{1}{12}$
81. **a.** $\frac{2}{3}$ **b.** $\frac{1}{12}$ **c.** $\frac{1}{3}$
82. \$$4\frac{1}{2}$ or \$4.50
83. **a.** \$63 **b.** \$40
84. \$240
85. \$18
86. $\frac{83}{120}$
87. **a.** \$120 **b.** \$1,500 **c.** \$2,000 **d.** \$2,380
88. $6\frac{2}{5}$
89. **a.** \$$10\frac{1}{2}$ or \$10.50 **b.** \$$1\frac{3}{4}$ or \$1.75 **c.** \$$23\frac{1}{2}$ or \$23.50
90. 75 kph
91. $66\frac{2}{3}$ kph
92. $74\frac{2}{3}$ kph
93. $7\frac{5}{8}$ inches wide and $9\frac{5}{8}$ inches high
94. $\frac{1}{2}$
95. **a.** 42 **b.** 35 **c.** 21 **d.** 14
96. **a.** \$$8\frac{1}{10}$ or \$8.10 **b.** The 10th copy cost you nothing. The price for 9 books would have been \$81 (i.e., 9 × \$9, no discount). The price for 10 books was still \$81 (i.e., 10 × \$9, less a $\frac{1}{10}$ discount, or \$90 – \$9 = \$81).
97. **a.** 69¢ **b.** 1012¢ or \$10.12
98. **a.** $\frac{5}{6}$ minute **b.** $22\frac{1}{2}$ minutes **c.** 1350 seconds
99. $2\frac{1}{2}$ hours
100. **a.** $\frac{5}{9}$ **b.** $\frac{4}{9}$ **c.** 5 to 4 **d.** 4 to 5
101. **a.** 30 **b.** 18
102. $\frac{1}{5}$, $\frac{3}{10}$, $\frac{7}{20}$, $\frac{14}{25}$, $\frac{5}{8}$, $\frac{2}{3}$
103. $28\frac{2}{3}$ cm wide and $44\frac{2}{3}$ cm long
104. $190\frac{5}{8}$ square feet
105. $81{,}807\frac{15}{32}$ cubic cm
106. **a.** $\frac{1}{4}$ **b.** $\frac{1}{8}$ **c.** $\frac{1}{16}$ **d.** $\frac{1}{8}$
107. \$1,250
108. **a.** $\frac{1}{3}$ pound **b.** $\frac{4}{15}$ pound **c.** He used $\frac{1}{60}$ pound more than $\frac{1}{4}$ pound.
109. 15
110. $54\frac{6}{11}$ kph
111. **a.** 20 **b.** 12 **c.** 31
112. $322\frac{17}{36}$ square feet
113. **a.** $4\frac{1}{4}$ **b.** $2\frac{1}{8}$ **c.** $1\frac{5}{24}$
114. **a.** $20\frac{5}{6}$ **b.** $26\frac{4}{5}$ **c.** 3 **d.** $8\frac{1}{3}$

CHAPTER 3 CONT.

115. $\frac{1}{4}$ inch
116. $\frac{3}{8}$ inch
117. $1\frac{1}{8}$ inches
118. **a.** 2,500,000¢ or $25,000 **b.** 250,000¢ or $2,500
c. 2,250,000¢ or $22,500
119. $\frac{1}{4}$
120. **a.** $14\frac{1}{4}$ inches long, $11\frac{1}{2}$ inches wide, $8\frac{7}{12}$ inches high
b. $1406\frac{19}{32}$ cubic inches
121. **a.** $\frac{3}{4}$ gallon
b. $2\frac{1}{2}$ gallons
c. $7\frac{1}{2}$ quarts
d. $2\frac{1}{4}$ gallons
122. **a.** $808\frac{1}{2}$ **b.** $57\frac{3}{4}$
c. 154
123. **a.** $10\frac{10}{11}$
b. $504{,}935\frac{5}{77}$
124. **a.** \$$1\frac{1}{3}$ or about $1.33
b. \$$270\frac{5}{6}$ or about $270.83
c. $276
125. **a.** $1{,}674\frac{1}{4}$
b. $558\frac{1}{12}$
c. $303\frac{1}{8}$
d. $367\frac{13}{16}$
e. $375\frac{15}{32}$
f. $1{,}046\frac{13}{32}$
g. $348\frac{77}{96}$

CHAPTER 4: DECIMALS

1. $10.87 (Note: As indicated in instruction E on page 106, gasoline charges are figured from pump readings, and these readings are usually taken as shown—i.e., rounded in the usual arithmetic methods.)
2. $6.53
3. 5.75
4. 56 minutes
5. 25 minutes
6. $193.17
7. **a.** .300 **b.** .364 **c.** .316
8. **a.** .5 pounds
b. $1.06\frac{1}{4}$ pounds
c. 121.6 ounces
9. 36¢
10. **a.** $21,850.92
b. $1,820.91
11. $3.35
12. 1.44 meters
13. $3.39
14. **a.** $13.29 **b.** $2.03
15. $1.29\frac{39}{209}$
16. $27.55
17. $2.16\frac{104}{231}$
18. $37.36
19. The first dealer's price was $237.81 higher.
20. 8.55 cm
21. **a.** .75 feet
b. $.66\frac{2}{3}$ feet
c. 40.8 inches
22. **a.** $1.75 **b.** $1.12
c. $2.87 **d.** $7.13
23. 5.3
24. $360.58
25. $21,598.20
26. **a.** $14.06 **b.** $14.24
27. **a.** $28.41 **b.** $9.47
c. $1.59
28. $36.74
29. **a.** $57,703.50
b. $51,903.50
30. $5.87
31. $1.28\frac{136}{1835}$
32. **a.** $14,924.52
b. $287.01
33. **a.** .75 years
b. $1.41\frac{2}{3}$ years
c. 140.4 months
34. 12¢
35. $9.72
36. **a.** 1,975 **b.** 1,264
37. 3
38. .5 cm
39. 10.6 cm
40. 13.4 cm
41. It totals 1.05 of the income. In other words, it accounts for spending more than they earn.
42. 519.2
43. **a.** $58 **b.** $43.50
c. $442.25
44. 2,045,319
45. 30
46. 178.125 square feet
47. 152.375 square feet
48. $11.02\frac{16}{17}$
49. 15 mpg
50. **a.** .25 hours
b. $1.33\frac{1}{3}$ hours
c. 165 minutes
51. $5.55\frac{7}{10}$
52. $33.33\frac{1}{3}$
53. $4.05
54. $33.95
55. **a.** 1.6 **b.** 3.4
c. \$$2.17\frac{11}{17}$
56. $36,144.75
57. 51¢
58. **a.** $1.07 **b.** $1.54
c. 19 minutes
59. **a.** $206.75
b. \$$895.91\frac{2}{3}$
60. **a.** .75 years
b. $1.44\frac{3}{13}$ years
c. 270.4 weeks
61. 204.14 miles
62. $28.47\frac{1}{17}$

CHAPTER 4 CONT.

63. .0678, .12, .2079, .275, .3
64. **a.** 6.75 **b.** 3.00 **c.** 3.75 **d.** 0.00
65. 3.75
66. $478.40
67. $6.36\frac{2}{3}$
68. $15.97\frac{1}{2}$ cm
69. **a.** $7,760,954.75 **b.** $3,256,892.10
70. **a.** $87.20 **b.** $261.60
71. $1.98\frac{46}{73}$
72. 482.5 kph
73. **a.** $.71\frac{3}{7}$ weeks **b.** $2.42\frac{6}{7}$ weeks **c.** 28.7 days
74. .7
75. **a.** $47.05 **b.** $32.70 **c.** $14.35
76. **a.** $11,337.15 **b.** $3,687.40
77. **a.** 3.75 **b.** $13.12\frac{1}{2}$ **c.** .75 **d.** $1.12\frac{1}{2}$
78. **a.** $258.72 **b.** $21.56
79. 49¢
80. **a.** .75 gallon **b.** 4.25 gallons **c.** 18 quarts
81. **a.** 2.429 **b.** 2.000 **c.** 3.667 **d.** 3.333
82. 1.4 cm
83. **a.** 2,510,534 **b.** 122,156
84. **a.** 446 **b.** 56 **c.** 73 **d.** 89
85. 6 mph
86. 1097.46 miles
87. 54.4
88. 9.3 cm
89. **a.** $3,768.35 **b.** $4,564.80 **c.** $126.80
90. **a.** 640 **b.** 832
91. 3.94
92. **a.** $4.41\frac{2}{3}$ hours **b.** $39.85\frac{5}{7}$ weeks **c.** $.76\frac{32}{73}$ year
93. **a.** 86.2 **b.** 86 **c.** 91
94. 41 cm long and 25 cm wide
95. 800 kph
96. $7.27
97. **a.** 141.75 **b.** 453.6 **c.** $2.82\frac{106}{567}$ **d.** $11.65\frac{65}{189}$
98. $228.27
99. **a.** $4.25 **b.** $4.25 **c.** $5.75 **d.** $2.75 **e.** $4.25
100. $7\frac{1}{2}$ hours or 7.5 hours
101. **a.** $1,315.21 **b.** $1,475.04 **c.** $122.92
102. **a.** .45 m **b.** 2.67 m **c.** 187 cm
103. 36
104. **a.** 13 liters **b.** 16.25 ml **c.** $1.53\frac{11}{13}$ ml
105. **a.** $13.02 **b.** $6.98
106. **a.** $237.50 **b.** $778.45 **c.** $75
107. **a.** 30.48 **b.** 91.44 **c.** $.39\frac{47}{127}$ **d.** $1.18\frac{14}{127}$
108. $5.07
109. **a.** 8 **b.** 88 **c.** 91
110. **a.** 1.25 feet high, 1.5 feet wide, 2.25 feet long **b.** 4.21875
111. **a.** 48 **b.** 88 **c.** 80 **d.** $.62\frac{1}{2}$ **e.** 62.5 **f.** 31.25
112. 3.354 square cm
113. 1.5625 square inches
114. **a.** $.07\frac{1}{2}$ km **b.** $1.77\frac{3}{5}$ km **c.** 3,250 m
115. $5.93
116. 14.33 cm
117. 22.7 liters
118. 2.5957 cm or $2.59\frac{57}{100}$ cm
119. $3
120. 144.5
121. 10.15 cm
122. $86.02\frac{14}{93}$ kph
123. 241.68 miles
124. **a.** 11.355 **b.** 17.411 **c.** $.26\frac{318}{757}$ **d.** $1.32\frac{76}{757}$ **e.** $1.05\frac{515}{757}$ **f.** $4.22\frac{546}{757}$ **g.** More than
125. 15 mph
126. 12.6 mpg
127. **a.** $122 **b.** $116.20

CHAPTER 5: PERCENTS 1

1. $273.60
2. $4,315
3. 7%
4. $1,200
5. $30,000
6. 15%
7. $305.20
8. $4,120
9. 4%
10. **a.** $\frac{2}{3}$% **b.** 2%
11. $280
12. 9%
13. $7,500
14. **a.** 40 **b.** 15% **c.** 6
15. **a.** 90% **b.** 90% **c.** 4 **d.** 10%
16. **a.** 16% **b.** 21 **c.** 4 **d.** 625% **e.** 525% **f.** 16%
17. **a.** $140 **b.** 2% **c.** 98%
18. **a.** 97% **b.** $6,800 **c.** $103\frac{9}{97}$% **d.** $204
19. **a.** $225 **b.** $150 **c.** $75 **d.** 1%; yes **e.** 97% **f.** $7,275 **g.** 98% **h.** $7,350 **i.** yes ($75)

CHAPTER 5 CONT.

20. **a.** 75% **b.** 25%
21. **a.** $\frac{1}{5}$ **b.** $\frac{4}{5}$
22. **a.** 80% **b.** 125% **c.** 20% **d.** 25%
23. **a.** 125% **b.** 16 mpg **c.** 80% **d.** 20%
24. **a.** 10% **b.** 20% **c.** 30% **d.** 40% **e.** 50% **f.** 90%
25. **a.** 120% **b.** 24 mpg **c.** $83\frac{1}{3}$ % **d.** 20%
26. **a.** $360 **b.** 9% **c.** 18%
27. **a.** 100% **b.** 100% **c.** 100% **d.** 100% **e.** 100% **f.** 100%
28. **a.** 22% **b.** 11%
29. **a.** $400 **b.** $800 **c.** $1,200 **d.** $1,600 **e.** $200 **f.** $600 **g.** $1,000 **h.** $1,400
30. **a.** $520 **b.** $6,500
31. 12%
32. **a.** $64.13 **b.** 103% **c.** 3%
33. **a.** $4,438.50 **b.** $177.54
34. $184.64
35. **a.** $66\frac{2}{3}$ % **b.** 150% **c.** 50%
36. **a.** 125% **b.** $12,500 **c.** 80%
37. **a.** 112% **b.** $18,750 **c.** $89\frac{2}{7}$ %
38. 56
39. 106
40. **a.** 110% **b.** 55
41. **a.** 110% **b.** 60 **c.** $90\frac{10}{11}$ %
42. **a.** 125% **b.** 25% **c.** 80%
43. **a.** 75% **b.** $20 **c.** 100% **d.** $133\frac{1}{3}$ % **e.** $133\frac{1}{3}$ % **f.** 75%
44. **a.** $\frac{3}{2}$ **b.** $\frac{1}{2}$
45. **a.** $3.75 **b.** $11.25 **c.** 75% **d.** $133\frac{1}{3}$ %
46. **a.** 60% **b.** 40% **c.** 40% **d.** $166\frac{2}{3}$ %
47. **a.** 75% **b.** 75% **c.** 75% **d.** 75% **e.** 75% **f.** 75%
48. **a.** 85% **b.** $117\frac{11}{17}$ % **c.** 15%
49. **a.** 1000% **b.** 10% **c.** 90%
50. .18 cm thick
51. .22 cm thick
52. **a.** 80% **b.** 20%
53. **a.** $75 **b.** $425 **c.** 85% **d.** $75
54. **a.** 86% **b.** $450 **c.** $116\frac{12}{43}$ %
55. $33\frac{1}{3}$ %
56. **a.** 16¢ **b.** 84¢ **c.** 13¢ **d.** $3.36 **e.** 25% **f.** $2.52 **g.** 75%
57. **a.** $\frac{19}{20}$ **b.** $\frac{1}{20}$
58. **a.** 152 **b.** 114
59. **a.** 75% **b.** 25%
60. **a.** 30% **b.** 70%
61. **a.** 48 **b.** 102
62. **a.** $15,000 **b.** $35,000 **c.** 70% **d.** 30% **e.** $42\frac{6}{7}$ %
63. **a.** 70% **b.** $60,000 **c.** $142\frac{6}{7}$ % **d.** $18,000
64. **a.** 20% **b.** 40% **c.** 60% **d.** 80%
65. **a.** 150% **b.** $2,250
66. $4,050
67. **a.** 140% **b.** $760 **c.** 40% **d.** $71\frac{3}{7}$ %
68. **a.** $\frac{9}{4}$ **b.** $\frac{5}{4}$ **c.** $\frac{1}{4}$
69. **a.** 25% **b.** 75% **c.** $10 **d.** $30
70. **a.** $40 **b.** 25% **c.** 75% **d.** 75% **e.** $133\frac{1}{3}$ %
71. **a.** $12 **b.** $28 **c.** 70% **d.** $142\frac{6}{7}$ %
72. **a.** 28 minutes **b.** 140% **c.** $71\frac{3}{7}$ %
73. **a.** 140% **b.** 18 min. **c.** 40%
74. **a.** 140% **b.** 35 minutes **c.** 14 minutes **d.** 40%
75. **a.** 125 % **b.** 25% **c.** 80%
76. **a.** 80% **b.** 20 psi
77. **a.** 104% **b.** 25 psi
78. **a.** 18 or $\frac{18}{1}$ **b.** $\frac{9}{5}$ **c.** $\frac{9}{50}$ **d.** $\frac{9}{500}$
79. **a.** 125% **b.** $10,000 **c.** 25% **d.** 80%
80. **a.** $4,400 **b.** $48,400 **c.** 110% **d.** $90\frac{10}{11}$ %
81. **a.** 70 or $\frac{70}{1}$ **b.** 7 **c.** $\frac{7}{10}$ **d.** $\frac{7}{100}$ **e.** $\frac{7}{1000}$
82. **a.** 110% **b.** $40,000 **c.** $4,000 **d.** 10%
83. **a.** $570 **b.** 40% **c.** $380
84. **a.** 40% **b.** $860 **c.** $516
85. **a.** $10 **b.** $2 **c.** $28
86. **a.** $20 **b.** $40 **c.** 80% **d.** $50 **e.** $70
87. **a.** 200% **b.** 300% **c.** 400% **d.** 500% **e.** 1100% **f.** 25,100% **g.** 389,700%
88. **a.** 25% **b.** $24 **c.** $18
89. **a.** $5 **b.** $15 **c.** 75%
90. **a.** 40% **b.** 60% **c.** $7.50
91. **a.** 50% **b.** $5 **c.** 200%
92. $4.30
93. **a.** $3.60 **b.** 60% **c.** 40%

CHAPTER 6: PERCENTS 2

1. 6 years
2. **a.** 50% **b.** 75% **c.** $83\frac{1}{3}$ %
3. **a.** 65% **b.** 35%
4. **a.** 741 **b.** 39
5. 94.9%
6. $6,489.60
7. **a.** $110 **b.** $121 **c.** $133.10 **d.** $146.41 **e.** $88 **f.** $29.70
8. $22.72 (Note: You may have to point out that a payroll office rounds such amounts to the nearest cent.)
9. **a.** 200% **b.** $66\frac{2}{3}$ % **c.** 50%
10. **a.** $16,632 **b.** 8%
11. **a.** $1,320 **b.** $1,080 **c.** $1,260 **d.** $1,206 **e.** $1,196.40 **f.** $1,800
12. 6
13. **a.** $63 **b.** $85.50 **c.** $99.90
14. **a.** $1,458.20 **b.** $4,881.80
15. **a.** $33\frac{1}{3}$ % **b.** $66\frac{2}{3}$ %
16. 28.8%
17. **a.** $3 **b.** $300 **c.** $2,557.50
18. $14,624
19. **a.** $12,000 **b.** She got nothing.
20. **a.** 50% **b.** 5% **c.** 45%
21. **a.** 20% **b.** 4% **c.** 2% **d.** 100%
22. **a.** $8\frac{1}{3}$ % **b.** 25% **c.** $66\frac{2}{3}$ %
23. $16.45
24. **a.** $50.40 **b.** $68.75
25. **a.** 25% **b.** 20%
26. **a.** $1,200 **b.** $1,320 **c.** $1,452 **d.** $15,972
27. **a.** $280 **b.** $840
28. 75%
29. **a.** 2,460 **b.** 8,240 **c.** 8,525
30. **a.** $9.45 **b.** $16.80
31. **a.** $244.20 **b.** $315
32. **a.** $1.20 **b.** $1.44, usually rounded to $1.50 **c.** $3.75
33. **a.** $1 **b.** $1.35
34. **a.** 24 **b.** 110
35. **a.** 25% **b.** 100% **c.** 250%
36. **a.** $107\frac{9}{13}$ % **b.** $7\frac{9}{13}$ % **c.** $92\frac{6}{7}$ % **d.** $7\frac{1}{7}$ %
37. **a.** $12\frac{1}{2}$ % **b.** 18% **c.** $22\frac{3}{5}$ %
38. She owes $531.
39. 50%
40. **a.** 14.2% **b.** 144 **c.** 24
41. **a.** 120% **b.** 20% **c.** $83\frac{1}{3}$ % **d.** $16\frac{2}{3}$ %
42. **a.** 10 **b.** 90
43. $66\frac{2}{3}$ %
44. **a.** 60% **b.** 10% **c.** 30% **d.** 60% **e.** 40%
45. **a.** 1200% **b.** 150% **c.** 50%
46. **a.** $4,000 **b.** $9,400
47. 72
48. **a.** $200 **b.** $450 **c.** $584 **d.** $862.50
49. 12%
50. **a.** 1% **b.** 13% **c.** 84%
51. **a.** 91 **b.** 160
52. **a.** 3,250 **b.** 1,500 **c.** 250
53. **a.** 66% **b.** 34%
54. **a.** $15.75 **b.** $60
55. **a.** 1% **b.** $1\frac{1}{2}$ % **c.** $\frac{5}{6}$ %
56. **a.** $33\frac{1}{3}$ % **b.** 50% **c.** $66\frac{2}{3}$ %
57. **a.** 18 minutes **b.** $37\frac{1}{2}$ minutes
58. **a.** $170,673.75 **b.** $112,601.40
59. **a.** 14 **b.** 30 **c.** 40
60. **a.** 4,860,000 **b.** 75,260,000 people
61. **a.** $77\frac{17}{29}$ % **b.** $12\frac{12}{29}$ %
62. **a.** 7,967 **b.** $6\frac{7}{10}$ % or 6.7%
63. 25%
64. **a.** 2% **b.** 50% **c.** 40%
65. **a.** 25% **b.** $62\frac{1}{2}$ % **c.** 150%
66. **a.** 5 hours **b.** 8 hours 20 minutes **c.** 4 hours 48 minutes **d.** 3 hours 20 minutes
67. **a.** $16\frac{1}{4}$ % **b.** $52
68. 84
69. **a.** 28 **b.** 120 **c.** 640 **d.** 252 **e.** 234
70. **a.** 18 **b.** $13\frac{7}{11}$ %
71. **a.** $450 **b.** $3,150 **c.** $2,475
72. **a.** $26 **b.** $52 **c.** $78 **d.** $130
73. **a.** 70% **b.** 30% **c.** $142\frac{6}{7}$ % **d.** $42\frac{6}{7}$ %
74. **a.** $3,037.50 **b.** $3,075.47 **c.** $3,152.83
75. **a.** $2.50 a pound **b.** $2.60 a pound **c.** $2.80 a pound **d.** $2.20 a pound
76. **a.** $1\frac{1}{2}$ % **b.** $4.83 **c.** $4.83 (Note: Such charges are made on the average unpaid balance unless the

CHAPTER 6 CONT.

entire bill is paid. An exception is made if an amount is unpaid because of a dispute in billing.)

77. **a.** $37\frac{1}{2}$ %
b. $62\frac{1}{2}$ %

78. **a.** See table below
b. It will be $132.04 higher at the credit union.

79. $1\frac{3}{7}$ %

80. $10\frac{7}{8}$ %

81. **a.** $66\frac{2}{3}$ %
b. $33\frac{1}{3}$ %
c. 150% **d.** 50%

82. **a.** $130.74 **b.** $217.75

83. **a.** $2,587.50
b. $14,789.50

84. **a.** $14\frac{2}{7}$ %
b. $12\frac{1}{2}$ %

85. **a.** $387.95
b. $969.86
c. $969.86
d. $38.79
e. $96.99
f. $135.78
g. $426.74
h. $1,066.85
i. $1,105.64

86. **a.** 400% **b.** 200%
c. $44\frac{4}{9}$ %

87. **a.** 3 (Note: You may have to point out to your students that it is not possible to sell just part of a new car.) **b.** 128

88. **a.** $55\frac{5}{9}$ %
b. $44\frac{4}{9}$ %
c. 180%
d. 80%

89. **a.** 5 **b.** 20 **c.** 60

90. **a.** 504 **b.** 1,740

91. $37.50

92. **a.** $14\frac{2}{7}$ %
b. $42\frac{6}{7}$ %
c. $85\frac{5}{7}$ %

93. They total over 100%. (Ask your students why such a result is not possible.)

94. **a.** 3.2 **b.** 50.4 **c.** 7.9
d. 127.0

95. **a.** 20% **b.** 6% **c.** 8%
d. 46% **e.** 13% **f.** 7%

96. **a.** 1.3 pounds
b. 3.7 pounds

78. **a.** Answer table

End of Quarter Number	BANK		CREDIT UNION	
	Quarterly Interest	Balance	Quarterly Interest	Balance
0	0	$6000.00	0	$6000.00
1	$75.00	6,075.00	$90.00	6,090.00
2	75.94	6,150.94	91.35	6,181.35
3	76.89	6,227.83	92.72	6,274.07
4	77.85	6,305.68	94.11	6,368.18
5	78.82	6,384.50	95.52	6,463.70
6	79.81	6,464.31	96.96	6,560.66
7	80.80	6,545.11	98.41	6,659.07
8	81.81	6,626.92	99.89	6,758.96

CHAPTER 7: MIXED CONCEPTS 1

1. 35
2. 3
3. 625
4. 24
5. $1\frac{1}{2}$
6. 22
7. 1174
8. 11
9. 90 miles
10. 25¢
11. 40
12. 2078 miles
13. 60
14. 30
15. 34
16. 1020 grams
17. 102
18. $1.20
19. 15
20. 360 feet
21. 375
22. 11
23. 36
24. 450
25. 63,360
26. 300
27. 71¢
28. $90.50
29. 14
30. $145.25
31. 85%
32. $3.10
33. $952
34. $7.50
35. 18
36. $11.97
37. **a.** $2.00 **b.** $33\frac{1}{3}$ ¢
c. 34¢
38. $1.55
39. 65
40. 520
41. $1\frac{1}{2}$ cups
42. $12\frac{1}{2}$

CHAPTER 7 CONT.

43. \$195
44. \$6.80
45. 600 km an hour
46. 4 seconds
47. 188
48. 4 hours 15 minutes
49. 4
50. 40
51. 60
52. 6.6
53. 240,000
54. \$3.90
55. 8
56. \$168
57. 671 miles
58. $8\frac{1}{2}$
59. \$62.40
60. 80 kilometers an hour
61. \$1,500,000
62. 225 kilometers
63. 2555 or 2562, depending on whether or not the year was leap year
64. \$88.36
65. \$3.33
66. 8
67. \$280
68. \$9.18
69. 8708 feet
70. 380
71. $14\frac{7}{12}$ ¢
72. 10 cm
73. \$11.11
74. **a.** \$1.27 **b.**\$1.28
75. 880 sq. ft.
76. 21.5
77. **a.** 10 cm **b.** 40 cm
78. **a.** 6 kg **b.** 9 kg
79. 40%
80. more than 2,916,666$\frac{2}{3}$ bushels
81. $133\frac{1}{3}$
82. 38.1
83. **a.** \$1.15 **b.** $57\frac{1}{2}$ ¢
84. 8,136,396 sq. km
85. 145
86. $62\frac{1}{2}$
87. \$8.40
88. 100
89. 61.2
90. 3,800,000
91. about 3,223,950
92. \$7.30
93. 12
94. \$724,832.21
95. 828
96. about \$4,656,862.75
97. $53\frac{11}{13}$ %
98. $559\frac{6}{13}$ sq. km
99. 171,429
100. $37\frac{1}{2}$
101. 28 cm by 38 cm
102. by 114,378
103. 25.1328 meters
104. 90
105. The first area is a square with each side 4 kilometers long, so it has an area of 16 square kilometers. The second area can be any shape and is 4 square kilometers in area. The first area is 12 square kilometers larger than the second.
106. 176,735.59 sq. km
107. **a.** \$24,161,000,000 **b.** $6\frac{489}{6431}$ %
108. **a.** about 24% **b.** about 5,520,000
109. 35,714
110. 110,942 sq. km
111. $55\frac{5}{9}$ %
112. 6156 cu. cm
113. 531
114. by about 1,540,000
115. $9\frac{13}{18}$ ¢
116. 7 strokes over par
117. 70 kph
118. 320 km
119. \$2.00
120. 307
121. **a.** 439 **b.** 1317
122. 2420
123. \$7.80
124. \$1,250
125. \$217.50
126. \$63
127. 7.2
128. 4 teaspoons of sugar
129. \$12.16
130. 54
131. $8\frac{2}{3}$ %
132. 28%
133. 54¢
134. \$11,200
135. about 15,789
136. $17\frac{1}{2}$ ft.

CHAPTER 8: MIXED CONCEPTS 2

1. 5 km
2. \$5.38
3. \$586.26
4. \$1,920
5. 448 sq. ft.
6. gross pay = \$224.80; federal income tax = \$40.46; state income tax = \$11.24; social security tax = \$13.71; union dues = \$2.25; net pay = \$157.14
7. **a.** $6\frac{2}{5}$ **b.** \$7.36
8. 50 words a minute
9. \$37.50
10. 720,000
11. 800 sq. cm
12. 80
13. She pays \$44.24 less if she pays cash.
14. $2\frac{1}{2}$ yards

CHAPTER 8 CONT.

15. The first brand is the better buy.
16. $20\frac{1}{2}$ hours
17. $1,170 (Note: This is a good opportunity to stress to your students that there are $4\frac{1}{3}$, not 4, weeks in a month.)
18. 4
19. 28
20. $21\frac{2}{3}$¢
21. **a.** neither **b.** The gold is heavier. (Note: An apothecaries' ounce is actually slightly heavier than an avoirdupois ounce.)
22. **a.** $6650 **b.** $4500
23. 6 hr. 33 min.
24. 5 hr. 27 min.
25. Jay; 1 hr. 6 min.
26. $197.75
27. $181.00
28. **a.** 80,776,500 **b.** 66,775,240 **c.** 40,926,760
29. **a.** 532 **b.** 266
30. .310
31. 11
32. 4,320
33. $2.27
34. **a.** $3679.97 **b.** $3692.98 **c.** salesman 2
35. 220,000 sq. cm
36. **a.** $\frac{14}{24}$ or $\frac{7}{12}$ **b.** $41\frac{2}{3}$%
37. $634.00
38. Mr. Whitney paid 40¢ more.
39. **a.** 14.20 **b.** 11.07 **c.** 97.5 **d.** 78.0 **e.** 886 ft. **f.** 1420 ft.
40. $937.73
41. 3 inches by $3\frac{3}{4}$ inches
42. **a.** 77.4% **b.** 77.4%
43. $1061.37
44. $19.00
45. She ends up getting the same amount for the money spent with both brands.
46. $35 billion
47. 89.4%
48. 9.0
49. 15 years 11 months
50. **a.** 19¢ **b.** $1.26 or $1.27, depending on whether the telephone company rounds to the nearest cent or charges the next higher cent for any amount which is not an exact number of cents
51. $350
52. 17.6 feet
53. 47% aluminum; 3.5% silica; 2% titanium oxide; 22% iron oxide; 25.5% water
54. **a.** $70 **b.** $334 **c.** $1,036
55. $215.35
56. **a.** $46\frac{3}{4}$ **b.** $42\frac{1}{2}$
57. $\frac{4}{5}$
58. **a.** 6579% **b.** $149\frac{23}{44}$%
59. $1,050
60. $846.75
61. **a.** 22 **b.** 400,000 **c.** 1,600,000 **d.** $72,727\frac{3}{11}$ **e.** $18,181\frac{9}{11}$ **f.** 4
62. $33,823,529,411.76
63. **a.** 4.8768 meters **b.** 19.5072 meters **c.** 121.92 meters **d.** 7 seconds
64. $27.43
65. 15,713,167
66. 2.32¢
67. 362 yards 1 foot 4 inches
68. 2; 3; 10; 3; 2
69. **a.** second size **b.** second size **c.** first size **d.** second size
70. $240
71. $7\frac{1}{2}$ hours
72. **a.** $465,113,920 **b.** $406,974,680 **c.** $1,773,246,820 **d.** $203,487,340 **e.** $58,139,240
73. $1.65
74. 16
75. **a.** $2,500 **b.** $700 **c.** $502
76. **a.** $24.50 **b.** $73.50
77. $292.50
78. 36 minutes
79. 25¢ (Point out to your students that stores do not round prices to the nearest cent but charge the next higher cent on any price which is not an exact number of cents.)
80. 25
81. 8 hrs. 45 min. or $8\frac{3}{4}$ hrs.
82. $38.75
83. $9.52
84. 7¢
85. $1,480
86. 1 cm in the drawing = 10 cm on the car
87. $59.23

CHAPTER 8 CONT.

88. $372.50
89. $68\frac{4}{7}$ kph
90. **a.** 2500 **b.** 750 **c.** 375 **d.** 1375

CHAPTER 9: MIXED CONCEPTS 3

1. 12
2. 464.9 mph
3. 15
4. 10
5. **a.** $6.50 **b.** $8.50 **c.** $21 **d.** $7.50 **e.** $13.50
6. 5
7. $660
8. 1 min. $42\frac{6}{7}$ sec.
9. 1250 km
10. $54\frac{6}{11}$ kph
11. 48¢
12. **a.** The $1\frac{1}{2}$ meter material will cost less. **b.** 75¢
13. 89,766
14. **a.** slower **b.** less **c.** The speedometer will show a speed less than the real speed of the car. The speedometer is set to register according to the rate at which the rear wheels turn. For each turn, the wheels are traveling farther with the large tires than they would with the regulation tires. Thus, when the speedometer is showing, say, 60 kph, the car is going farther than 60 kilometers every hour and so is traveling faster than 60 kph
15. 795 ft.
16. $148.57
17. **a.** $143.88 **b.** $11.88
18. the 2-scoop cone
19. **a.** 75 lbs. **b.** 200 lbs. **c.** at most 1 foot from the rock **d.** 4 feet
20. **a.** $27\frac{1}{2}$ feet **b.** 125 cm
21. **a.** 9,460,716,019,200 km **b.** 8 min. $18\frac{18349}{18737}$ sec.
22. 3647.6 cu. cm
23. **a.** $7.50 **b.** $1.50
24. 13
25. **a.** $11\frac{1}{9}$ **b.** $17\frac{11}{17}$ **c.** 25 **d.** $33\frac{1}{3}$ **e.** $42\frac{6}{7}$ **f.** 50 **g.** $66\frac{2}{3}$ **h.** 100 **i.** 200 **j.** 300
26. **a.** $150 **b.** 19¢ **c.** $1.42
27. $2\frac{1}{4}$
28. 28
29. **a.** $2.65 **b.** $4.30 **c.** $6.62 **d.** $8.14 **e.** $12.04 **f.** $3.19
30. See table below
31. See table below
32. **a.** 504 cu. ft. **b.** $7\frac{7}{8}$ cu. ft. **c.** 64, but they must be stacked on their sides rather than on their bottoms **d.** none
33. **a.** 8 hr. 20 min. **b.** 72 km an hour
34. **a.** 504 cu. ft. **b.** $9\frac{3}{16}$ cu. ft.

30. Answer table

Date of Payment	Total Payment	Interest	Principal	Balance Due
3/15	Amount Borrowed			$500.00
4/15	$90.00	$9.00	$81.00	$419.00
5/15	$90.00	7.99	82.01	336.99
6/15	$90.00	6.80	83.20	253.79
7/15	$90.00	5.56	84.44	169.35
8/15	$90.00	3.89	86.11	83.24

31. Answer table

Date of Payment	Total Payment	Interest	Principal	Balance Due	Part of Month
3/15	Amount Borrowed			$500.00	---
4/10	$90.00	$ 7.55	$82.45	$417.55	26/31
5/20	$90.00	10.63	79.37	338.18	40/30
6/25	$90.00	7.92	82.08	256.10	36/31
7/15	$90.00	3.73	86.27	169.83	20/30
8/25	$90.00	5.15	84.85	84.98	41/31

40. Answer table

	Hourly Rate	Sun.	Mon.	Tues.	Wed.	Thurs.	Fri.	Sat.	Straight Time	Time and a Half	Double Time	Gross Pay
a.	$4.50	0	8	8	8	8	8	0	40	0	0	$180.00
b.	$4.50	0	10	8	8	8	8	0	40	2	0	193.50
c.	$4.50	0	0	8	8	8	8	8	32	8	0	198.00
d.	$4.50	8	8	8	8	8	8	8	40	8	8	306.00
e.	$4.50	8	10	12	8	6	10	10	38	16	10	369.00
f.	$4.50	8	8*	10	10	8	10	8	32	14	16	382.50
g.	$5.82	8	8	10	8	8	8	10	40	10	10	436.50
h.	$6.75	0	0	0	10	12*	10	10	16	12	14	418.50
i.	$7.85	2	8	8	7	9	10	6	39 3/4	10	2 1/2	469.04

CHAPTER 9 CONT.

c. 48, whether they are stacked on bottoms, sides, or ends.
d. 63 cu. ft.

35. **a.** 426.5 mph (Note: Since St. Louis is on Central time and Detroit is on Eastern time, the flight time was 1 hr. 5 min., not 2 hr. 5 min.)
b. 426 mph

36. $508.45

37. $192.50

38. **a.** 600 sq. ft. **b.** 1080 **c.** 90 **d.** $157.50

39. $224\frac{95}{144}$ sq. ft.

40. See table above

41. The number of hours to be paid is shown in the table at right.

41. Answer table

Problem	a.	b.	c.	d.	e.
Hourly Rate	$5.76	$8.19	$7.75	$4.50	$5.10
Sun.	0	7	5 + 3.7	5 + 3.8	5 + 3.5
Mon.	3.6 + 4	4 + 4	5 + 3.7	5 + 3.8	5.1 + 3.6
Tues.	3.8	4	0	3.7 + 4	0
Wed.	0	0	3.9	0	0
Thurs.	4	0	0	0	4.9
Fri.	0	0	4	0	0
Sat.	5	4	2.9	0	0
Standard Time	15.4	12	15.9	15.7	12.9
Time and a Half	5	4	3.6	.8	.7
Double Time	0	7	8.7	8.8	8.5
Gross Pay	$131.90	$262.08	$299.93	$155.25	$157.85

CHAPTER 9 CONT.

42. **a.** $12 **b.** $10.50 **c.** $17.10 **d.** $11.40 **e.** $24.38 **f.** $9.10.

43. **a.** Score = 178
See table below
b. Score = 188
See table below
c. Highest possible score = 300
See table below

43. a. Answer table

1	2	3	4	5	6	7	8	9	10	Total
5 4	7 /	X	8 /	X	X	X	7 /	6 3	4 3 —	178
9	29	49	69	99	126	146	162	171	178	

43. b. Answer table

1	2	3	4	5	6	7	8	9	10	Total
X	X	7 2	6 3	9 /	9 /	8 /	X	X	8 / 9	188
27	46	55	64	83	101	121	149	169	188	

43. c. Answer table

1	2	3	4	5	6	7	8	9	10	Total
X	X	X	X	X	X	X	X	X	X X X	300
30	60	90	120	150	180	210	240	270	300	

